Hamlyn

Tales of
the Uncanny

Tales of the Uncanny

Václav Černý
Zlata Černá
Miroslav Novák

Hamlyn

London · New York
Sydney · Toronto

Translated by Helen Notzl

Designed and produced by Artia for
The Hamlyn Publishing Group Limited
London · New York · Sydney · Toronto
Astronaut House, Feltham, Middlesex, England
Copyright © Artia 1976
Illustrations © Jaroslav Šerých 1976
Graphic design by Aleš Krejča
Copyright © this edition:
The Hamlyn Publishing Group Limited 1976
ISBN 0 600 38716 X
Printed in Czechoslovakia
1/02/03/51

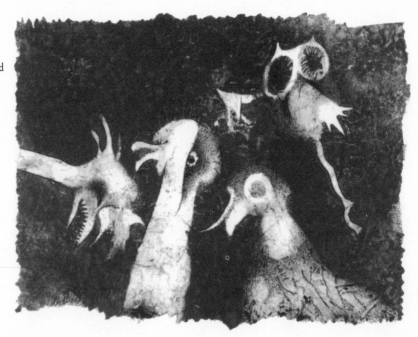

Contents

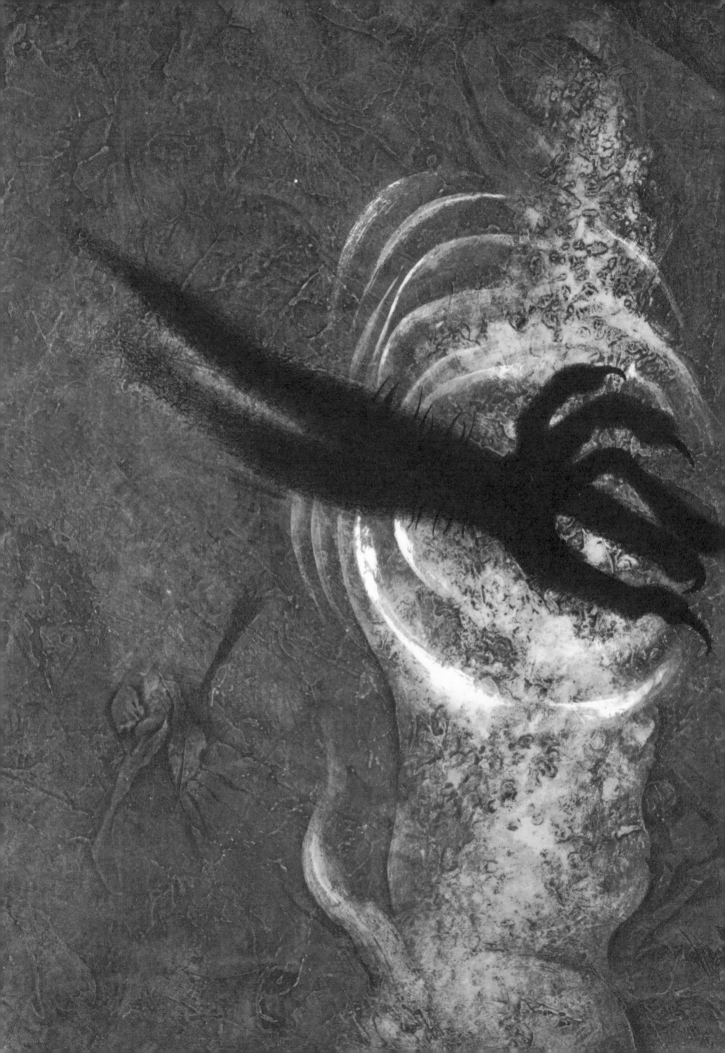

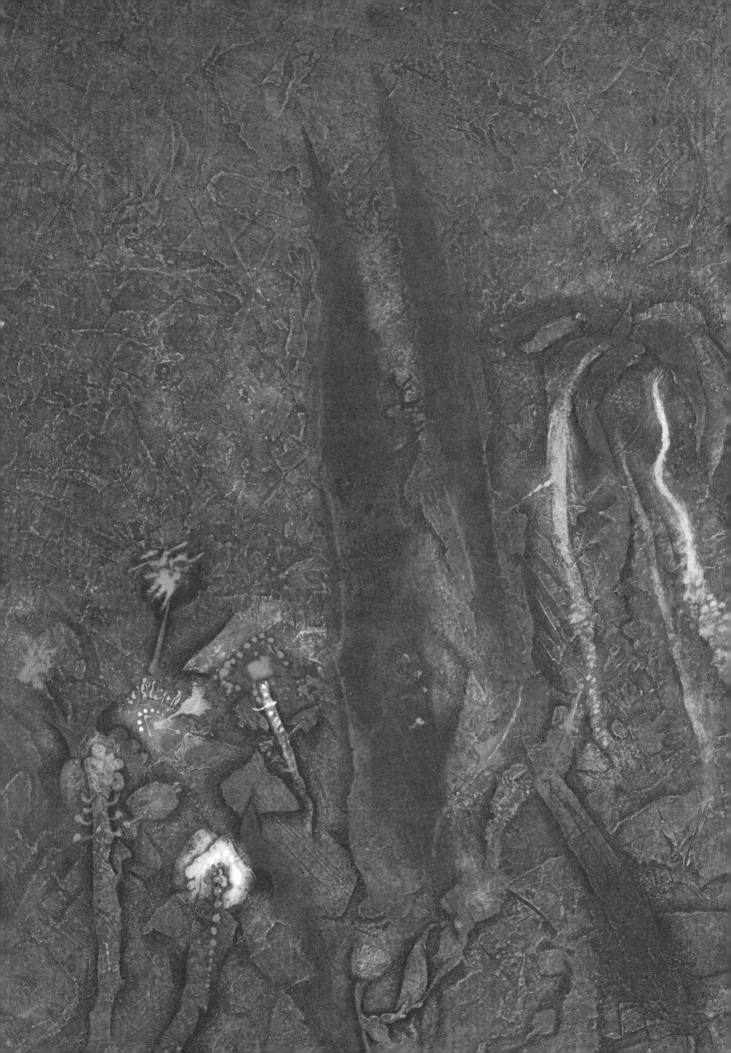

Monsters
on the Retreat

*M*odern civilization is disturbing the mysterious silence of dark forests, deserted mountain tracks and treacherous swamps. So few opportunities of meeting a ghost or a monster remain. And even in these dark and dangerous places where at least some reference to them has been preserved, no one is really afraid of them any more.

In the past, however, the world positively teemed with monsters and supernatural occurences. Every grandmother frightened her listeners with endless tales about them.

In this book, we have selected and retold genuine folk tales which have been handed down from generation to generation, be it with icy shivers down the back or with a smile! We have tried to evoke these gruesome, mischievous and even romantic monsters and ghosts from all over the world in the spirit of their native lands.

The Silver Forest

People have always been lured by the mysteries of deep, shadowy forests from the beginning of time. As long as they gathered the fruits of the forest, or felled trees in clearings dappled by the sun or on the forest's edge, they felt content. But when the path led deeper into the shadow of the forest, uneasiness fell upon them. Here the mysterious gloom thickened and boulders covered with moss loomed up in the path. The surface of murky pools no longer mirrored the blue sky. Only an occasional breath of air or the splash of frogs disturbed its sombre calm. The lonely cry of birds and the cracking of dry twigs were the outward signs of the hidden life of the forest.

Not only did shy animals hide in the green half-light, but also mysterious beings lived here. These beings were seldom in sympathy with people. Phantom lights in the swamps tempted the wanderer from the safety of the dry paths; ugly wild-women lurked in the deserted glades. Their wild dancing caused the death of anyone who joined them and did not succeed in escaping in time.

A thousand dangers threatened any man who boldly entered the twilight of the forest. And only very few ever succeeded in reaching the place where beautiful wood-nymphs gathered for their songs and dances under the tall spreading oak tree whose leaves shone with gold. So strictly did they guard their secrets, that every dare-devil who spied on them was cruelly punished. And yet sometimes the nymphs took pity on a lonely hunter or a lost wanderer and took him or her amongst themselves as a brother or sister. Songs were sung about such people, even though they spoke reluctantly of their adventures.

In one village, there lived an old man who had an only son

named Dushan. The father was a wise and intelligent man and so he did not make Dushan stay at home with him. When he grew to the age when he could support himself, his father sent him out to gain experience of the world.

'There are many people in the world, and many trades and much useful knowledge. Go and discover for yourself what is right for you. When the time comes, you will return home.'

So Dushan went. He walked through villages and towns, he met Christians and Turks. He studied various trades, but in the end his heart was captured by the violin. From the moment that he succeeded in playing it, he never again parted with his violin. Whenever he was grieved by the avarice of men or the injustice of their lot, he took out his violin and played until his sadness passed. And he loved to play it just as much when the sun shone brightly and gaily dressed girls danced in a circle.

In his travels Dushan learned many things and he understood many things, but still he did not feel that the time had come for him to return home. His hands were just as empty as when he had left and he had nothing remarkable of which he might be proud.

And so he wandered on. Once, when he had left a noisy city behind him, he was attracted by a soft green footpath. He turned to follow it and walked until he came to a forest. Silence encompassed him, disturbed only here and there by the cry of jays. Dushan lost track of time and of the way back and he let himself be carried on by the hushed pathways, trodden down by animals.

The sun had already set long ago and the forest had grown dark. Shreds of light white mist rose from the ground to hang among the trees. Suddenly a bright moon rose above the tall trees and in that instant the forest was utterly transformed. The trees towered high, their leaves shone with gold and their trunks glistened with ancient silver. Smoke was rising above the trees, and the flames of a fire flickered in the distance. Dushan caught a glimpse of strange beings dancing around the fire. They were winged maidens dressed in long flowing dresses.

Dushan started in fear. At once he remembered the many tales he had heard about evil wild-women and beautiful but cruel wood-nymphs. He did not dare to approach the fire, but at the same time he was loath to forego this wondrous sight. So after a moments hesitation he sat down quietly at the foot of the spreading oak tree under which he stood and watched, spell-bound, to see what would happen.

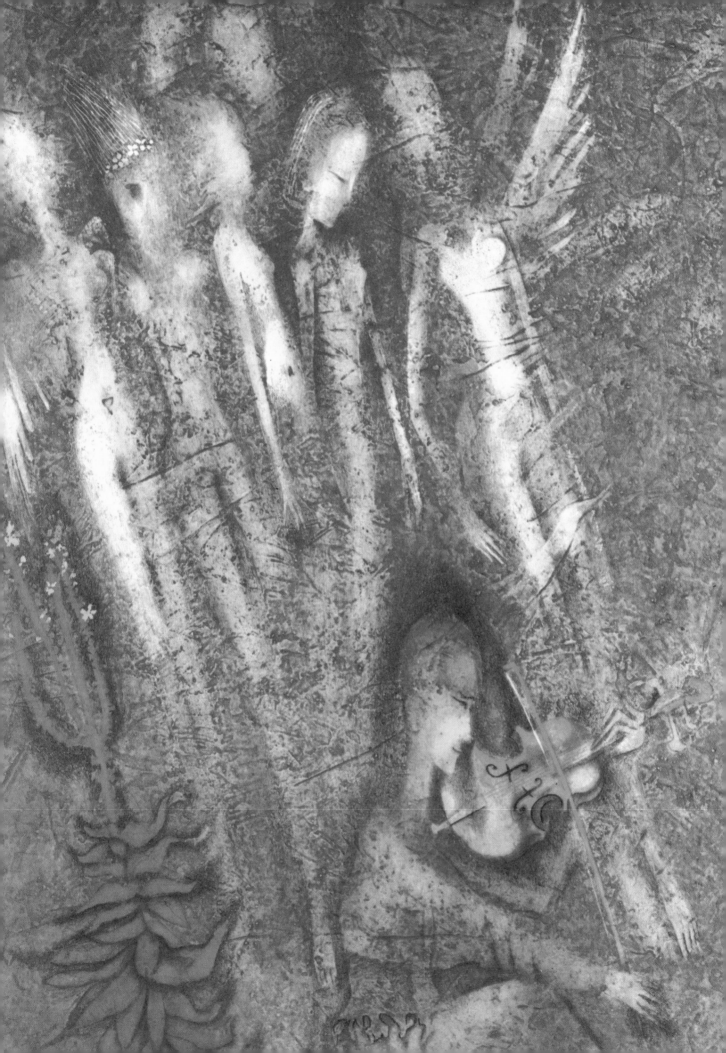

A group of winged maidens drifted away from the fire and slowly moved closer to the place where he was hidden. The maidens were dancing in the light of the moon, crossing from the darkness of the tree's shadow into the moon's bright radiance, their long dresses catching on branches and merging with the white mist. A gentle singing accompanied their dancing. Dushan could not restrain himself and at the sight of such beauty, he sighed aloud.

Instantly there was pandemonium among the nymphs. Their singing stopped abruptly and the air was awhirl with the beating of their wings. The nymphs searched for the intruder who had stolen into their midst. The dark shadow of the spreading oak tree did not protect Dushan. The nymphs caught sight of him and in the very same moment all of them fixed him in the stare of their evil eyes. At that moment Dushan found that he could neither speak nor see.

He found himself in total darkness and he could not even plead for mercy. His lips were unable to move and in vain, he stretched his arms out to where he believed the nymphs were. They no longer paid any attention to him and began to dance once more. Dushan began to weep, for there was no help for him now, and he must perish wretchedly in the depths of the forest.

Suddenly he remembered his violin. It would tell his tale of sadness to these heartless creatures. He settled down beneath the tree and began to play. He played in the dark forest and in the bright light of the moon, though he saw nothing of it. He told of the beauty which he had allowed to entice him, wistfully he sang of his pain and his grief. The nymphs stopped their dancing and listened to Dushan's song.

When he finished playing, they darted off into the forest and searched for healing herbs which would break their spell. One applied the healing balm to his eyes, another brought healing water and gave it to him to drink. Dushan's vision and speech were restored. The nymphs took him amongst themselves as a brother and he stayed with them for a long time and accompanied their dances with the song of his violin.

After many years he returned to the world of people and to his native land. But it is not without reason that people say that the forest leaves its mark on a person to the end of his days. Dushan was often silent; it seemed as if he lived in another world. And year after year he would disappear into the forest for days on end.

The Devil
Wedding

Aluda Sazikauli lived at the edge of the village of Shatili. He
had neither wife nor children, his father and brother had
been killed by Kists, and his mother had died of fever during a
pilgrimage to the Cross of Gudan. Aluda took his revenge on
the murderers of his father and brother, provided for the
funeral of his mother and from that time he lived alone. He
was respected by the villagers, for he was a good hunter and an
amusing drinking companion, who always knew how to add
to the general good cheer with a fine story. 'To the Cross of
Gudan,' he would say, 'you should have been with me and
now you could make me choke on every lie you catch me
telling. Can I help it if you are all so unadventurous?'

One day Aluda Sazikauli set off to hunt mountain goat.
There were great numbers of these shy creatures on the
distant mountain slopes. He travelled until dusk, and spent
the night under his cloak in a sheltered valley by a spring. The
next day he climbed the bare mountains. Boulders jutted out
from the rock-face like the teeth of a fairy-tale giant, but not a
mountain goat was to be seen. He crossed over the summit
and descended into the next valley, but again he had nothing
better to eat but bread, cheese and water from a spring. In vain
did he call on Ochopinto, the herdsman of the wild animals of
the forest. By late in the afternoon of the third day he had seen
nothing. Then suddenly he saw three nanny-goats and a
mighty he-goat with powerful horns standing outlined
against the sky. Taking cover behind boulders, he crept close
to them, and felled the he-goat with a single shot. The third
night was fast approaching, and he could not spend the night
on the bare mountainside. He put the mountain goat on his
back and began to climb down the steep slope.

Suddenly in a narrow valley, between the trees, he saw

smoke rising, and before long he came to an extraordinary building. It was a stone castle made of rough-hewn boulders. The castle was built right into the hillside and had a crumbling watch-tower. A drawbridge led to a wooden portico, guarded by twin towers. The castle was gigantic. Its doors were so huge that a rider with his spear held high could pass through them, and two knights in armour could ride side by side along the battlements.

'To the Cross of Gudan,' said Aluda Sazikauli to himself. 'There are no castles built like this, today. Our ancestors must have been mighty men!'

The light was fading and smoke was rising from the chimneys. Singing could be heard from the great hall and Aluda longed for a warm hearth where he could rest his weary limbs. Easing the goat from his shoulders, he called, 'Masters of the house!' There was no reply. He called a second time, and there was no answer. When he was about to call for a third time, the door opened. Dusk had fallen and Aluda thought that his eyes were deceiving him in the gathering darkness. Out of the house and down the lowered drawbridge came a man with seven heads. The heads twisted in every direction

and they spoke one after the other in the same voice: 'Welcome, guest! Come in and accept the hospitality of this house!'

At that moment, Aluda realized that he stood before the terrible seven-headed devil, Baqbaq, whose very name cast fear in the hearts of ordinary men. Aluda was frightened, but it was too late to draw back and decline the invitation. 'May the White Rider help me,' he thought to himself as he stepped bravely toward the seven-headed monster.

'I see you are a hunter.' The devil laughed so heartily that the valley shook. 'I shall call my son to take care of your prey.' He turned two of his heads and called into the house. The door opened once again, and his son stepped on to the drawbridge. He was even more misshapen than his father; he had three legs and his arms brushed the ground.

'This is my youngest son, Forest-Howler,' said Baqbaq. 'My son, take our guest into the hall.'

'Come in, my guest,' Baqbaq turned to Aluda. 'You are not the only one who will be feasting under my roof tonight. We are celebrating the marriage of my daughter, Three Eyes-Beautiful Eyes. I am sure you have heard of her.'

Aluda was terrified but all the same he smiled politely and followed Baqbaq and his son into the castle. They passed through an anteroom and entered the great hall. A cauldron hissed and steamed above a great fire that roared in the hearth. The guests were sitting on benches along the walls, and they fell silent as Baqbaq led Aluda inside.

'Our house has been honoured by a new guest,' said Baqbaq, 'a Khevsur hunter. I don't know your name, guest,' he turned to Aluda, 'but I see by your weapons that you are a brave man, and a mighty hunter.'

Aluda turned a little pale, but his host continued:

'You may put your weapons aside, because you are safe in my house.'

Aluda drew back a pace, but he was instantly surrounded by hideous claws that reached out towards him. 'Entrust me with your gun and scimitar, so I can hang them in a place of honour.' It was Baqbaq's middle son, Mangy-Polecat who spoke. Reluctantly Aluda placed his gun in one of the claws, even more reluctantly he unbuckled his scimitar and put it in the second claw, and then the third claw seized him and stood him in the centre of the room.

'Allow me to introduce my guests, Khevsur,' said Baqbaq. 'I am sure you have never met any of them before.' Baqbaq laughed in all his seven throats, and the company joined him until the rafters shook with their roaring. It was, indeed, fine company. There were fewer of them by far than there were heads; they stared at Aluda out of many eyes; they stretched out so many arms that Aluda thought that they could have taken Ananuri Castle apart stone by stone before he could count to five.

'You should tell us your name, guest,' said the ghastly Thundershaker, who was presiding over the wedding feast, 'so that the bride and groom may later remember this day with pride.'

Aluda Sazikauli hesitated. If he told them his real name they would come to visit him and the rest of the villagers would avoid his house in horror. He would become an outcast in his native village, and mothers would frighten their children with his name. He made up his mind to lie to them.

'My name is Seven-Devils-Enemies-of-the-Gods,' he said.

'You have a strange name for a Khevsur,' said Thundershaker in surprise. 'I have met a great many of your fellow countrymen, and they had all sorts of names, but I have never heard of anyone with a name like yours. We know that Khevsurs swear to the Cross of Gudan. You ought to do so now, so that we can believe you.'

The rest of them joined their voices to his until an indescribable uproar set in.

'To the sock on the gam, my real name is Seven-Devils-Enemies-of-the-Gods,' Aluda hurried with his response before the noise had quietened. No one heard him properly, and so everyone believed him.

The master of ceremonies then called for silence. He delivered a toast and handed Aluda a goblet of arrack. The goblet was as big as a warrior's helmet, but without batting an eyelid Aluda drank it all. The devils growled in admiration and Thundershaker called out:

'Bring me the cauldron and I shall give our guest a portion of honour!'

At once Baqbaq's sons jumped forward and handed him the huge, steaming cauldron from the fire. Thundershaker fished something out onto a dish. Forest-Howler knelt down beside Aluda and placed the dish before him. Aluda saw that the dish contained a human head. He blenched and his hands began to shake; he tried to swallow but his throat was dry and he felt nausea rising in his throat.

Baqbaq was watching Aluda's expression intently, and he guffawed with all his seven mouths:

'It seems you do not feel well, guest. Surely you do not

19

mean to say that the food I offer you does not appeal to you?'

'Actually, I have lost my appetite today,' lied Aluda. 'I tired myself out with my long journey, and your portion of honour seems a trifle too rich for my stomach, weakened as it is with hunger. If you would not be offended, I would prefer some cheese which I brought with me.'

All the demons present began to bawl at the top of their lungs, but it appeared they were not offended by the refusal. On the contrary, they were bubbling over with sympathy, and each was recommending his own proven remedy against nausea.

'The best is snake's bile,' screamed a toothy goblin from the corner.

But the seven-voiced Baqbaq shouted the rest of them down: 'Give him a vat of beer, that will restore his appetite.'

Everyone agreed and at once they brought a full vat. They held it to his mouth and poured the beer into him until he thought he would drown. With all his might he pushed Forest-Howler away who thought Aluda wanted him to pass the vat around the circle. The demons drank, a river of beer gurgled down their throats, and soon they had to bring another vat. The beer tickled their palates, and they began to pat their furry bellies, and all at once they burst into their own wedding song:

'Ho, ho, hyde,
We have a bea-oo-tiful bride.
She's lovely and furry from head to toe,
Hunchbacked, warty and pigeon-toed.
The bridegroom comes from far away,
And he's even furrier, hey, hey, hey!'

When they thus reminded themselves of the bride, Thundershaker bellowed out once more:

'Show our bride to the guest, for that is our custom. He is a human and he will spread tales of her beauty among his people.'

They all agreed, and as one body they led Aluda to the bride's chamber. There sat Three Eyes-Beautiful Eyes surrounded by her bridesmaids. She was not as hideous as Aluda had feared, in fact she would even be quite comely if she could only hide her third eye.

'Be in good health, beautiful bride,' Aluda greeted her. 'Never did I see a more beautiful devil bride. I never would have thought that devil maidens were so beautiful.'

'I like you too, guest,' said Three Eyes-Beautiful Eyes, and when none of her bridesmaids were looking she added: 'You are almost as fair as I, and fairer by far than my groom. You are no doubt courageous and they told me you are a good hunter. I am sure you could support a loving wife and a family of devil children. Kidnap me!'

'How could I dare to do such a thing?' Aluda protested. 'I would insult the house in which I was made welcome, and I would make blood-feud enemies out of my friends.'

'But you said that I appealed to you, and I want you,' Three Eyes-Beautiful Eyes stamped her foot stubbornly. 'I shall order my maid to saddle a horse secretly and you will kidnap me.'

Aluda refused, he resisted, why he even tried to run away, anything to escape from this two-fold danger, but all in vain. Three Eyes-Beautiful Eyes snatched him up and tucked him into her sewing basket, and then she whispered something to the hideous old woman who was her maid. In a little while she released him and took him out into the courtyard and through the wicker gate, into a pasture where a saddled horse stood waiting.

At that moment joyous shouting burst out from the front of the house. The groom had arrived to claim his bride. Aluda was scared beyond thinking. What was he to do? He could see no way of escape. Before very long the wedding guests would discover that the bride had disappeared, and he with her. They would pursue them both, and he had no means of fighting them. And even if he did manage to escape how could he live with a wife like Three Eyes-Beautiful Eyes?

Three Eyes-Beautiful Eyes, noticing his dejection, snuggled up to him and said:

'You kidnapped me and I can never return to my father's house. But I shall defend myself with you and if worse comes to worst, I shall die with you. For didn't you say that you were fond of me?'

From the house came the wailing of the bridesmaids, and the terrible roar of the frenzied wedding guests, and above it all the dreadful voice of the insulted bridegroom thundered out:

'Who has kidnapped my bride?'

'Seven-Devils-Enemies-of-the-Gods,' answered all the demons at once, one louder than the other.

'Even if there are fourteen of them, or even twenty-one,' swore the groom, 'not one of them will escape me. I shall tear every one of them into a thousand pieces!'

Aluda tried to hide behind a boulder, comforting himself that they might overlook him, but Three Eyes-Beautiful Eyes misunderstood his intention; she leaned against the boulder, for she thought he wanted to roll it down on the house. She wrenched an enormous crag out of the mountain-side, and the crag went surging down towards the house below with a deafening roar, tearing down everything in its path. Then she snatched Aluda under one arm, the horse under the other and bounded up the mountain slope.

When the crag crashed into the castle below, caving in the walls, the devils set up a terrible howling. Only the groom lost no time and stormed after the runaways up the mountainside.

'Ha, now I've got you,' he called out behind them in a thunderous voice. 'Stand still, all seven of you!'

Three Eyes-Beautiful Eyes set Aluda and the horse down and leaned against another boulder. In the dark she could not see who was where, and the devils could not see her.

By the sound of the shouts, though, it was apparent that they were not far behind them. Three Eyes-Beautiful Eyes rolled another boulder down the mountainside and the groom roared out in rage and in pain.

'What is the matter with you?!' asked Baqbaq's seven heads.

'Nothing, but I am becoming more and more cross!' said the groom, not wanting to confess pain in front of his father-in-law.

And the narrow valley replied to his thunderous voice with the echo:

'Cross . . . cross . . . cross . . .'

'Ha, there is that Khevsur,' said the devils who were higher up the mountain. 'He's swearing to Gudan's Cross!' And they started to topple boulders down in that direction. Those who were lower down picked up rocks and pelted them uphill, all of them bellowed, those who were hit roared out, rocks rumbled and trees cracked. No one knew who was fighting whom in the confusion.

Aluda took his chance and jumped up on the horse and started out on the narrow sheep trail along the mountain precipices quite unmindful that with every step he could break his neck, while the devils battled amongst themselves mercilessly. Perhaps they all truly believed that their adversaries were enemies of the gods, or perhaps in their boundless rage they wanted to revenge themselves on their comrades for the blows they had received. Who can say?

Suddenly, the voice of Thundershaker boomed out of the valley:

'Ho, ho, not one of you will escape! I know what I shall do!'

He stepped up to the side of the mountain, leaned his mighty shoulders against it, braced his feet against the opposite precipice and leant so mightily that the side of the mountain cracked and collapsed, its peak tore off and buried the entire valley. For miles around the earth shook, the mountains twisted, and in the fissures new valleys appeared. And from that spot where the terrible horde of devils lay buried, there rose a column of dust and acrid smoke as if from burning limestone.

But by then, Aluda was in safety. At that very moment he was crossing the mountain pass, and carefully he guided his horse through a narrow gorge between two escarpments and down into the valley which he knew well.

Wild Goose Bay

One day in the spring, when the ice and snow had receded inland and all the coast was fragrant with the smell of fresh growth, Niarqoq was returning in his kayak from the hunt. He found it strange that he did not see his wife on the cliffs for she always came to watch for him. He was even more puzzled when his two children did not come running to meet him.

He hurried home and found only his old mother there. He questioned her about his family and his mother said:

'This morning your wife went with the children to watch the northbound flight of the wild geese. A great flock was passing overhead and it suddenly swooped down to the ground and encircled them like a cloud. Then the flock rose up again but your wife and children were no longer there. So the geese probably carried them away to the north.'

When Niarqoq heard this, he said to his mother:

'Then I shall go to the north to look for my wife and children.'

He dressed in his best furs, put on his firm sealskin boots and set off towards the north. He walked and walked, and after he had walked a very long time, he came to a dark pass. He heard terrible cries as he entered it.

Niarqoq walked on, for there was no other way he could go, and when he came closer he saw that two colossal naked bodies were standing in his way. The giants were fighting and shouting abuse at each other. Niarqoq hid behind a rock and wondered what he should do, for these two apparitions stood in his way. The giants took no notice of him; they kept on fighting and swearing at one another without moving from the spot. Niarqoq noticed that there was a narrow gap between them and he decided to slip through, for he was anxious to go on. Carefully he moved closer to the two giants, but just as he was about to slip into the chink between them, he heard a whizzing sound and a tuft of torn-out hair as thick as ropes fell at his feet.

Niarqoq started in fright, but since he was already going, he clambered over the hair and squeezed himself through the gap between the two giants. Suddenly he saw an enormous hand reaching down towards him. He threw himself to the ground, the hand missed him and rose again into the hair of its opponent. Niarqoq jumped up and ran away; he ran as long as he heard the cries and the cursing behind him.

Then he walked and walked again, and after he had walked a very long time, he saw a yellow light in front of him. Then he walked on a little more, but soon he saw that he could go no further, for his way was obstructed by an enormous seal-oil lamp. The lamp burned with a great flame, it shone and hissed, but Niarqoq was impatient to go on. He climbed up on the lamp, warily stepped down on a large piece of blubber as if on to a piece of melting ice, and forded the lamp on it to the other side. Hardly had he climbed down again, when the lamp suddenly turned off and vanished.

And again he walked and walked, and after he had gone a great distance, he saw a cloud of steam rising before him. He went on and in a little while he heard a loud bubbling noise.

When he came a little closer to the cloud of steam, he heard a voice from within, saying:

'I am cooking soup and I eat human beings.'

Then Niarqoq saw that a huge cauldron was standing in his path, and pieces of meat as large as boulders were bubbling in the kettle and sending up clouds of steam. Niarqoq wanted to continue his journey north, so heedless of the danger, he cautiously stepped down on a piece of boiling meat and hopped across from one piece of meat to another, as if from one ice floe to another. The meat was churning in the boiling water and it was fatty and smooth. Several times he slipped and almost fell, but finally he managed to reach the other side and continued on his way. The voice from within the cauldron called out behind him: 'If you return, you will not escape from me again,' and vanished.

Niarqoq walked and walked, always further toward the north. Little by little the green vegetation dwindled and in the distance in front of him he saw the grey and white outlines of icebergs. But then he saw that a stream flowed across his path and a strange figure stood on the opposite bank of the stream. It was a fat old man with large ears. He stood with his back to Niarqoq and powerfully brandished an axe. He was chopping down the trunk of an old willow tree and the chips flew on all sides. And whenever a chip fell into the stream, it was instantly changed into a salmon which flashed swiftly away to the sea.

Niarqoq told himself that the old man would be offended if he approached him from behind. So he carefully walked around the old man in a wide arc, so that he could not be seen. Then he walked towards him from the front and realized that it was the spirit Qajungajugssuaq.

Qajungajugssuaq did not stop brandishing the axe and cried angrily:

'You dared to approach me from behind.'

Niarqoq replied:

'No! Surely you can see that I am coming towards you.'

'All the same I know very well that you came from behind me,' Qajungajugssuaq snapped. 'And for that I shall kill you.'

'If you wish to kill me, then kill me. But first tell me whether you saw my wife and children. The geese carried them away from my home to the north and I am going to search for them.'

The old man burst out laughing:

'Following the geese north! You will never get there unless I carry you. Come here!'

When Niarqoq came closer, the old man threw aside his
axe, took him by the hand and said:

'Close your eyes and do not open them until I tell you to,
no matter what happens.'

So Niarqoq closed his eyes and felt a violent gust of wind
lifting him into the air and carrying him away. He heard the
roaring of the sea and the whistling of the wind. He also heard
snorting and a curious flapping sound. It occurred to him that
Qajungajugssuaq was probably creating the wind with his
huge ears and he dearly wished to take a look, but then he
thought better of it and closed his eyes even tighter.

They flew a long time in the icy wind, until at last the wind
died down, Niarqoq felt firm land beneath his feet and then he
heard the voice of the old man:

'You may open your eyes now.'

So he opened his eyes, but the old man was nowhere to be
seen. He looked about and saw that he was standing on the
shore of a great bay. The bay was surrounded by rocks and
crags and not one green leaf was to be seen. Beyond the crags
there was nothing but ice and snow.

He saw a large group of strange people dressed in clothes
made of feathers standing by the water's edge. They had
expressionless faces; round, fixedly staring eyes, and between
their eyes long thin noses jutting right out from their
foreheads, curved a little at the end. They looked like nothing
that Niarqoq had ever seen. They walked about and took no
notice of him.

Niarqoq did not know what to do. Helplessly, he looked around until he heard a familiar voice behind him:

'Daddy, have you come to visit us?'

He turned and saw two small figures just like the rest. He knew they were his children by their voices.

'Come, let us go to mummy,' said the children and led him under an overhanging ledge where his wife was sitting. She, too, looked just as strange as the children and he only recognized her by her voice. But his wife lashed out at him cruelly:

'You should not have come looking for me. I like it here and I do not want to look at you any more. Go away, you are ugly!'

And so Niarqoq sheltered under another ledge and the children divided their time between him and their mother. The rest of these strange people took no notice of him as before.

One morning his children came running to him. They were frightened and said that something had happened to their mother. They cried to him to come quickly to look at her. She was lying under her ledge and Niarqoq knew that she was dead. He was standing over her sadly, wondering what could have happened to her, when he noticed that a disturbance was growing up around him.

The people who had taken no notice of him before suddenly began to examine him; they moved closer until they surrounded him from all sides. Then one of them cried out: 'You have killed her!'

The rest of them took up the cry; they glared at Niarqoq intently with their unmoving eyes, craned their necks out toward him and pushed closer and closer. They gathered from all over the bay; there were ever more and more of them and their cries echoed into the distance. When it seemed that the crowd was about to pounce on Niarqoq, they suddenly froze and fell silent. In the next instant these people changed into wild geese. The huge flock ascended and honking angrily, flew away.

Niarqoq was left quite alone on the silent, desolate, rocky shore between the grey sky and the grey sea. Suddenly Qajungajugssuaq appeared before him and said:

'Do not think that they have departed. More of them will return and they will try to peck you to death. You must defend yourself. I have brought you a whip made of willow. Sit down over there on that rise and wait. But remember, you must not fall asleep.'

Niarqoq obeyed. For a long time, nothing happened. When his eyes were beginning to close with fatigue, a huge black cloud appeared on the horizon and was swiftly coming closer. It was an enormous flock of geese. Honking angrily, they swooped down on Niarqoq from all sides. He brandished the whip with all his strength and slowly the geese began to dwindle until finally not one remained.

Niarqoq sat down to rest, but the old man appeared once again, and reminded him, 'Take care that you do not fall asleep!' Then he disappeared.

So Niarqoq struggled to stay awake and before long a large grey cloud appeared on the horizon. Again the flock of geese swooped down upon him, but this time they were fewer in number. Niarqoq withstood them, but his weariness began to overtake him and Qajungajugssuaq came once again to warn him not to fall asleep.

With a great effort Niarqoq resisted sleep until finally on the horizon a white cloud appeared and an even smaller flock of geese flew towards him. There were also two little ones among them. They did not attack Niarqoq like the rest, but stayed to one side and watched. By this time Niarqoq was extremely weary and it took him a very long time to overpower the flock. In the end, only the two little geese remained, then they rose up and flew away. And Niarqoq sank to the ground and slept.

When he awoke, he was along on the shore surrounded by silence and darkness. He sat down and thought about everything that had happened. Suddenly Qajungajugssuaq appeared and said:

'So now you see how it all turned out.'

Niarqoq did not know what more he could do, so he stayed there with Qajungajugssuaq.

The Unexpected Visitor

M r Shirozaemon always knew how to keep his shop stocked with the very best varieties of tea and so he prospered. His shop was full of assistants and there were as many maids and servants in his home as in a modest nobleman's residence. The maids were supervised by the eldest amongst them, the housekeeper Takae, and the youngest was her fifteen-year-old-niece, Okame, who was the mistress' chambermaid.

Okame was a very pretty, happy young girl. She got on with everyone and indeed, she was the darling of all the family and servants, for everyone felt in better spirits when Okame smiled.

One day, early in the spring, Mr Shirozaemon's household was full of work and bustle. They were making great preparations for the celebration of the Spring Festival of Maidens. Everyone was tidying and cleaning. Festive clothing was taken out of the chests, and in the kitchen they were preparing rice cakes spiced with green spring herbs for the festival.

Okame was the happiest person in the household. Her merry voice could be heard all over the house, she laughed so gaily that it seemed that her preparations were more like play than work. In the afternoon, a strange change came over her. Suddenly she fell silent; she would stand without moving; then again for no apparent reason she would run off and hide, and things would fall from her hands.

The first to notice the change in her was her aunt, the housekeeper Takae, and she asked her whether anything was the matter. Okame did not reply; she ran away and hid somewhere. When later she upset a vase and scattered the flowers in the courtyard and then crawled under the

verandah, the maids began to whisper that Okame was probably not a person at all, but a fox – foxes know how to be masters of deceit when they want to! The old cook, who did not like all this turmoil and whispering, finally said it aloud:

'It seems to me that Okame is in fact a fox. She wormed her way in amongst us and wants to put us all under a spell. Everyone take a stick and let's drive her away!'

'How could she be a fox,' said Takae angrily. 'Why I have known her since her birth and I brought her here from our village. The poor thing is probably ill.'

But the girl grew worse and worse, and when the rest of the maids became frightened of her, Takae began to be really worried so she asked her mistress to send for the exorcist. They both thought that he might be able to find out what had happened to Okame.

When the exorcist arrived, the women all sat in a circle with Okame in the centre. The exorcist walked around Okame three times and chanted magic words. Then he sat down opposite Okame and fastened his eyes on her. At first the girl did not even move but suddenly she bowed her head and spoke out in an utterly strange voice:

'I am the fox Rin and I took possession of the body of this girl. I came to you like this because I am very hungry and you have so much good food here. Give me a few of those fragrant green cakes and I shall go away again.'

The cook, who was actually rather jealous of Okame because she was always so merry, did not like this at all. So she spoke out at once:

'Now I understand it. A fine fox. That sweet-toothed Okame has invented all this so she can taste the cakes before the day of the festival! Don't give her a thing!'

But no one listened to her and Takae herself quickly brought a tray of cakes and placed them in front of the girl. She reached for them at once and gobbled down five cakes as if she had not eaten for at least three days. Then she remained motionless, as though nothing happened. After a moment the exorcist asked her:

'What more do you want, Rin? You did promise that you would go away.'

Okame twitched and answered in that unfamiliar voice:

'Those are good cakes, they are so festive. I enjoyed them very much. But I have a family of five children and we would also like to celebrate the Festival of Maidens. My grandmother has never tasted such exquisite cakes, so give me some to take with me on my way and I shall truly leave.'

33

'I should say they are delicious cakes,' the cook again spoke up. 'You are not likely to find cakes like these anywhere else. But to waste them on foxes is a shame. Give her nothing and thrash her!'

But the mistress of the house ordered her to bring a whole bowl of cakes. Takae tied the cakes into a little bundle and placed them in the girl's lap.

Okame bowed and spoke for the third time in that strange voice:

'I thank you kindly on behalf of myself, my children and my grandmother. I am very grateful to you for your kindness. And now, please drive me out!'

The exorcist nodded to Takae and she stepped up to the girl, shook her fist at her and cried out:

'Go away, Rin, run away and do not show yourself here again!'

Suddenly Okame jumped up and began to run away. But she had hardly taken a few steps, when she stumbled and fell. In a trice she picked herself up, looked around and said in her usual voice:

'Whatever is happening? Is something wrong? Why are you all staring at me? Why I only slipped and fell!'

'Look over there!' the exorcist pointed outside. They saw the fox Rin dart around the corner with a bundle of cakes in her jaws.

And so everyone was convinced and all were happy that Okame was certainly not a fox, for after all, one fox would surely not possess the body of another fox!

The Valley of Hungry Demons

There was once a young man who lived high in the mountains, where the peaks were lost in the clouds. He was as big and as strong as three men, but he was far from handsome. He had a strikingly large head and for that reason he was called Bullhead. He avoided people and people avoided him. Who can actually say why, perhaps because of his ugliness or perhaps there was some other reason. All the same a fine and valiant heart flamed in his breast and Bullhead longed to use his strength in a way that would be of service to humanity, although he shunned human company. So he decided that he would dedicate his life to the battle against evil demons, before whose gluttony no living being was safe. It was because of them that the fertile valley was deserted; the original settlers had perished and no one dared to follow them.

For a long time Bullhead walked alone in the mountains until one day, on the edge of a forest, he met a morose young man. Bullhead struck up a conversation with him and learned that he was called Delger the Solitary. One thing led to another and before long the two agreed to form a bond of friendship and help one another in their battle against evil demons.

It was not long before they met another young man, lank and thin, with a pallid green complexion like grass. His name was Delger like Grass and he joined the friends. In the evening, as they were preparing to lie down and sleep under a spreading oak, they saw that a man with a face as white as snow was sitting on one of the branches. He called himself Delger from the Tree and he, too, made a pact of friendship with them.

The next morning they all continued on their way. They

climbed down into a valley which echoed with the roaring of a river as it tumbled over boulders. On the opposite bank of the river they could see a small homestead. When they came closer, they realized that it was abandoned. No one answered their calls, the only sound they heard was the bellowing of hungry cattle from the fold. Not one person appeared in the valley during that day, so the friends made up their minds that they would settle here for the moment; they would soon see what the future would bring.

Every day, three of them would go off hunting and the fourth would stay home to take care of the cattle and prepare the food.

One day it was Delger the Solitary's turn to be on duty at home. He saw to the cattle, lit a fire under the kettle and put some meat to cook. Then he prepared some airan, a drink made of milk. He was so absorbed in his work that he did not notice a tiny old woman come towards him. She was only about one ell tall and she carried a large pannier on her back. It was so huge that she could hardly be seen underneath it.

'Give me a little meat and a drink of the airan,' she begged.

Delger the Solitary did not say a word. He gave the old woman a piece of meat and poured her some milk. No sooner had the old woman tasted the food that she suddenly vanished and with her the kettle of meat and the prepared airan.

Delger the Solitary was ashamed that he had let himself be tricked by the old woman. He could not possibly tell his companions, whatever would they think of him! So he found some horseshoes in the bar and made tracks with them around the house, one over the other. Then he took a bow and shot arrows at the house until the quiver was empty. He had scarcely finished preparing all this when his friends returned from the hunt and looked for their food.

Delger the Solitary frowned:

'Can you not see what has happened here? A horde of robbers attacked me, I barely managed to hold my own against them. But they did manage to make off with the kettle full of food and the airan.'

His friends praised him for his courage and went to bed.

The next day, it was Delger like Grass's turn to be on duty and he fared just as Delger the Solitary. Hardly had the tiny old woman taken a bite of the meat, than she disappeared and with her the kettle of meat and the airan. Delger like Grass could not think of a better idea than taking the horse-shoes and tramping the area around the house with them. Then he shot a quiver full of arrows at the house. Just as he finished

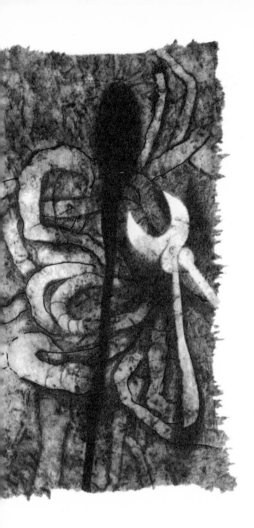

arranging all this, his companions returned and they searched for their food. And Delger like Grass presented them with the same story as had Delger the Solitary.

Nor on the third day when Delger from the Tree was on duty did he fare any differently. And when they had all gathered together in the evening, Delger from the Tree said:

'We shall have to leave if robbers are running riot here!'

Bullhead calmed them down and told them not to be hasty. The next day he would be on duty and then they would see what happened if the robbers returned.

The next day, when the Delgers went off into the mountains, Bullhead kindled the fire, put some meat into the kettle to boil and was preparing the airan. Just as the meat began to smell delicious, the tiny old woman with the huge pannier on her back appeared in front of the house and begged for a little food. Aha! So these are the robbers, thought Bullhead, and aloud he said:

'I shall give you as much meat as you want. But all the water has boiled away, so leave your basket here and bring me a little water.' And he handed her a bucket which had no bottom.

The old woman said nothing, laid down her basket and went outside for the water. Bullhead watched her through a chink in the door. As soon as she walked down the steps, the old woman stretched herself up so tall that her head was lost in the clouds. She planted her feet wide apart and bent for the water from the middle of the river. She drew a full bucket but before she could lift it, all the water ran out. So she bent over once again. In the meantime, Bullhead leapt quickly to her basket to see what was inside.

In it lay a strong rope braided from human veins, a pair of iron tongs and a heavy iron crowbar. Bullhead hurriedly exchanged the rope for an ordinary one made of yak hide and he replaced the tongs and crowbar with wooden ones – at that moment the old woman returned. She threw the bucket at his feet.

'I shall never draw anything with this bucket, it has no bottom. Now give me a piece of meat and some milk!'

Bullhead refused. Instantly the old hag swelled up until she almost filled the room. Then she proposed:

'Very well, do not give me anything. Let us wrestle together. If I win, you belong to me, and so does everything else around here.'

Bullhead agreed. The crone pulled the rope from her basket and said the first contest would be to see who could tie the other up the most firmly.

37

'I shall tie you up first!'

She seized Bullhead with her huge claws and tied him up securely. Bullhead took a deep breath, flexed all his muscles and the soft rope of yak hide yielded.

'And now it's my turn!'

He took the rope of strong human veins and tied her fast. She puffed herself up, trying to stretch in width or in height, but the rope would not yield. The old crone admitted defeat. Then she proposed the next contest. They would pinch one another with tongs and the one who could not endure it was the loser. Bullhead agreed.

The crone seized the tongs and rushed at Bullhead. But he only taunted her, saying that she was only tickling him. After all this was not supposed to be part of the contest. When he attacked her with the heavy iron tongs which he squeezed with his strong arms, the old hag began to shriek with pain and admitted at once that she was defeated.

And so she proposed the final contest. Each of them would take his crowbar and would strike the other with all his might.

The old hag swelled herself up to an enormous height, seized the crowbar from her basket and raised her arms high into the air to strike. Bullhead swiftly put the iron crowbar into the red-hot fire and leapt aside. The old hag smote into the fire with all her might until the sparks flew all over the room.

'Be careful,' he shouted at the hag. 'You will set the house on fire, and that was not a part of the agreement.'

'You be careful!' shrieked the hag. 'This is no contest. Stand still, otherwise I cannot hit you!'

So Bullhead stood still and the hag raised her arms and hit

38

him on the head with all her might. His head spun and he could scarcely see, but he quickly called out:

'And now it is my turn!'

He seized the red-hot crowbar and hit the hag on the head. She roared out in pain and her cries were so loud that the trees bent and she took to her heels in flight.

In the evening when the Delgers returned from the hunt, they found the kettle full of meat and the airan ready.

'Just come along and have a look at your robbers,' Bullhead challenged them and led them along the tracks which the hag had left behind her. The tracks led them to the foothills of the mountains and into a deep cave, where they found the hideous old hag dead.

'No doubt she was one of those demons who held sway here in this valley and devoured the farmers in the house where we live,' Bullhead told them. 'From this day forth there will be peace in the valley, so we shall have nothing more to do here. Would you like to stay and farm here, or will you journey on with me, fighting against demons?'

The Delgers reflected; they would be sorry to give up the wealth that they had found. They would be able to marry and have children, why then should they journey on through unknown regions fighting against demons, when there were so many of them that they would never destroy them all?

Bullhead did not try to persuade them, it was probably his fate to remain alone. He bade them farewell and with his bow and quiver and the heavy iron crowbar, he set off higher into the mountains.

Lovers
of Ambrosia

In the city of Basra, a company of scholars regularly assembled, each of whom was learned in the sciences and brilliant at discussion; but more than all knowledge, they appreciated food and drink. For this reason the name of the company was Lovers of Ambrosia. One day a sage from distant Maghrib visited Basra and strayed into the woods to the glade where this company had gathered. He asked if he might join their circle and take part in their discussions. Together they spoke of the sciences; nor did they leave out questions of religion and law. Then the stranger said:

'I have heard many wise words, today. However, on one subject, learned gentlemen, I should still like to hear your opinions: whether ifriti grow old as humans do and whether their evil increases or decreases as they grow older.'

Ridwan ash-Sharki, who was presiding over the meeting of the Lovers of Ambrosia, answered:

'Neither in the Koran nor in any other trustworthy books is anything stated about ifriti being born or dying. One must take it that they came into being at the same time as angels, and so they are of the same age. Because the goodness of angels does not vary in its extent, then, without doubt, ifriti, too, are constant in their evil.'

Ibrahim ibn Abu Ibnihi al Kamari wiped his mouth and put forward an objection:

'The character of demons does not depend, as is well known, on their essence, but rather on this: whether they accepted or rejected the teaching of God. Their character is, therefore, by nature dissimilar to the character of angels and cannot be judged in the same way. What is true of angels cannot be true of ifriti and vice versa.'

Zaid ibn Umar al Bahri, who was called ar Ra'is spoke:

'Fakhruddin ibn Dja'far al Barri told me a story which he heard from Nasra ibn Sa'id ash Shimali, which Abdullah ibn Hasan al Djanubi had related to him as follows:

'A certain pilgrim made a pilgrimage to Mecca and on the return journey, he left the caravan with which he had been travelling and set off alone toward the mountains. There were no springs in that region and robbers and wolves raged there. All of a sudden the pilgrim caught sight of a huge throng of people burdened with heavy loads. There were many women and children on carts and donkeys. The throng were heading towards the desert.

The pilgrim was astonished and asked one of the leaders where they were going. The man pointed ahead and said: 'There!'

The pilgrim asked whether they had come from a country that had no water. 'Nowhere is there water more sweet than in the city from which we have come,' replied the man. 'Then are enemies moving towards your city and you are threatened with being overwhelmed in war?' the pilgrim asked. 'There are no cities more safe against enemies than is ours,' replied the man. 'Why then are you abandoning the security of your homes and going into the desert, where only the insecurity of a camping ground and the fury of wild beasts await you?' the pilgrim asked. 'It is not good to ask about things which should best be left unsaid,' the man replied. And then the throng

continued on its way, passing by the pilgrim. When the last of these people disappeared over the horizon, the pilgrim said to himself: 'I must visit this city in order to see what is driving so many people from their homeland.' And he mounted his horse and rode off in the direction that the throng had come.

He rode all day and spent the night in the mountains. Towards the evening of the following day he saw an imposing city before him. It was rich with vegetation and safeguarded by numerous towers and fortified stone walls. He rode into the city through one of the gates and saw shops full of luxurious goods and parks with splashing fountains. The squares of that city were like the court-yards of sultans' palaces and in each quarter there was a beautiful mosque with an exquisite minaret. Each mosque had a school attached to it, but everything was deserted and there was not a living soul to be seen. The pilgrim rode through the streets and passed through the squares and wondered at all the beauty around him.

Later when evening came, he went into one of the inns, so

he might eat and sleep. The larder was full of food and jugs of precious wines stood in the cellars, but there was no sign of the innkeeper anywhere. 'By God,' said the pilgrim to himself, 'only a madman would turn his back on all this abundance!' He dined lavishly and after reciting his prayers went to bed.

The following morning he rode through the streets again, but this time he noticed something that had escaped his attention the previous day: the trees in the parks were cracked as if by a sudden tornado, the walls of the houses were battered and the severed tips of minarets were lying scattered on the ground. 'La haula wa la kuwwata!' the pilgrim said to himself. 'Verily, I do not know what force could have done this!'

Later when noon was approaching, he returned to the inn where he had spent the night, to eat. He tied his horse in front of the door and entered the courtyard alone, intending to wash himself at the well. All of a sudden it seemed as if an enormous cloud blotted out the sun and everything was covered in shadow. The pilgrim looked up and saw a huge figure towering above the city like a gigantic mountain. It had a clean-shaven head and its hips were girded with leather. The face of the giant was beardless and its expression was not of anger, but rather a sort of childlike wonder was reflected in his eyes. For a while he stood sucking his thumb, thick as the stump of a mighty oak; then he put his left hand on his hip and swinging his right foot, kicked at the dome of the bath-house as boys do when they play rugger.

The pilgrim was terrified by this apparition; and he also feared being struck by one of the boulders wrenched from the buildings, for they were flying through the air all around him. He darted into the inn and ran to the door to bring his horse inside so that the giant would not see him. At that moment he saw an enormous hand pushing aside the roofs and it seized his horse as if it were some sort of insect. The pilgrim's curiosity got the better of him, and he looked out from under the staircase and saw that the monster was lifting the horse to his eyes and was moving its head back and forth while trying to tear out its legs. As long as the horse writhed, the giant was amused, but when the mutilated horse died, he threw it aside and looked about for a new toy.

The giant squatted above the street, which instantly grew dark, and shaded his eyes with his hand while he carefully inspected the spot where he had taken the horse. The pilgrim was beside himself with fear, but he did not dare to make the slightest move. Nevertheless it seemed that he had not escaped the prying gaze of the monster, for he began to snap the chimneys off the surrounding buildings and to throw them at the door and into the courtyard of the inn, as boys do with stones when they are trying to drive a mouse out of the bushes so they can catch it.

The roof of the inn caved in from the terrible blows of those chimneys and the staircase where the pilgrim was crouching trembled. Terrified that he would be buried by the stone staircase, the pilgrim took advantage of a moment when the giant was reaching for more chimneys to hurl at the inn.

Jumping from his hiding place, he ran through the door and dashed to the building opposite, where he hoped to find more reliable refuge. It was probably an arsenal, built of mighty ashlars which could withstand the impact of battering rams. But what are all the inventions of war against a giant's strength! As soon as he caught sight of the pilgrim, the giant stepped forward and with a powerful swing of his foot, kicked into the front of this sturdy building. But it was not Allah's wish that the pilgrim should be harmed. The giant stubbed his toe, which was probably not as tough as the rest of his body. At once a stream of blood spurted out, flooding the street, rushing into cellars and tearing down the walls around the gardens. And then something happened which the pilgrim had not expected: for a moment the giant stared in surprise at his bleeding foot, then he grimaced, opened his mouth wide, and a flood of tears burst from his eyes which he smeared all over his cheeks with his dirty hands. Finally, he ran off crying and sobbing to rinse his wound in the spacious pool in front of the palace of the city's ruler.

The pilgrim made use of this opportunity. He fled from the city and wandered for some days, thirsty and without food in the surrounding mountains, until at last he came upon a caravan which escorted him in safety to the place where he had originally intended to visit.'

'This, then, is the story which I heard from Fakhruddin ibn Dja'far al Barri, to whom it was told by Nasra ibn Sa'id ash Shimali who originally heard it from Abdullah ibn Hasan al Djanubi. And so I ask myself, could this terrible giant be none other than the ifrit child, who probably still as a suckling babe was caught by the great Sulaiman, who trapped him in a bottle, sealed it with his ring and flung it into the sea? Then, no doubt some unsuspecting sailor fished out the bottle and released the ifrit. He then, deprived of the care of a loving mother, wandered into that very region and amused himself playing with that city. Verily, how vast is the world and how countless are its mysteries. And so, if I may touch upon the question bestowed on us by our learned guest, I say: What will that ifrit do when he grows up and stops playing attention to scratches? Will not the evil which he commits be greater than that which he commits today?' And the stranger parted from them, saying:

'You have instructed me and now I am leaving to return to the land from whence I came, in order to meditate upon laws which are subject to so many interpretations.'

The Lovers of Ambrosia continued their feast, paying attention rather to emptying the bottoms of their dishes than to the grains of truth in the story Zaid ibn Umar al Bahri, known as ar Ra'is, had related, for they knew that a fabrication pertinently used is more convincing than the most truthful of truths!

The Son
of Old Wolf

In a village called Marsh Green, there lived two brothers of Old Wolf's line. The villagers felt that the elder brother had not yet earned the name which his father had given him at the time of his birth, and so they called him simply Son of Old Wolf. The younger brother had earned their respect, for although he was lame, nevertheless he was a deft wood carver, and they called him by his rightful name – Happy Dog.

At one time, the Son of Old Wolf was to have been married, but on the eve of the wedding, his bride was stolen from him. He set out to hunt the kidnapper and rescue the maiden from him. But days later he returned, alone and without his sword. From then on the villagers considered him a coward and everyone avoided him. So he hitched the horses to his two-wheeled cart and drove away, travelling upstream along the banks of the river called Swift Water and into the mountains where he would make his home. Happy Dog followed him, for he was also affected by the disgrace. They built a round hut at Pebble Brook and there they lived. They saw no one; from time to time a cousin would come on his horse, bringing them salt, millet and tobacco.

The Son of Old Wolf would go off into the forest to hunt and often stayed away for several days. His brother Happy Dog minded the house and occupied himself with his craft.

One evening, after they had gone to bed beside the slowly dying fire, the Son of Old Wolf heard a sound as if something was circling the house. He thought perhaps he had been dreaming. But then besides the regular breathing of his younger brother, he clearly distinguished a snorting sound coming from the other side of the wall. Deciding it must be a bear or some other beast of prey, he seized a glowing log from the fire and stepped outside. When he had swung the log a few times and it burst into a bright flame, he saw a half-erect figure standing in front of him in the darkness, staring at him with bloodshot eyes. Taking it for a bear raised up on its haunches and just about to spring on him, the Son of Old Wolf flung the burning log at it. The creature snarled in fury, turned, and with peculiar swinging jumps, ran off towards the forest. There it stopped, stretched its forepaws high above its head and roared at the Son of Old Wolf in a voice that was neither human nor animal. In that instant, the Son of Old Wolf knew that this was no bear. Then the beast caught a low branch in his paws and swung off into the forest.

The Son of Old Wolf sat up for the rest of that night. In the morning, when day had scarcely dawned, he examined the footprints of this strange beast and discovered to his astonishment that they were like the prints of a human being. He made up his mind to get to the bottom of this mystery and when Happy Dog awoke and lit the fire to cook breakfast, the Son of Old Wolf said to him:

'Sharpen the axe, brother, and lend me your sword.'

'I thought you were going hunting, brother,' said Happy Dog, surprised at this request.

'You know well, brother,' the Son of Old Wolf cut him short, 'that it brings bad luck for men going off into the forest to speak their reasons for doing so.'

Happy Dog asked no more, but sharpened the axe, took his sword and its belt down from the hook and handed them to his brother.

The Son of Old Wolf set off into the forest. There were only a few tracks, but all led into that part of the forest where he had never ventured. For a long time he went through thick undergrowth, then he scrambled up steep slopes, clinging to the roots of trees, until at last at the close of day he came to a clear stream in a small green valley. The land rose gently from the stream, and the Son of Old Wolf made camp and set down his felt cloak and satchel and went to explore his surroundings.

He saw a mud-hole where wild boars came to wallow, and deer trails leading to water. He made up his mind to hunt one for his supper. Sure enough, before long, a graceful roe ran out of the forest. The Son of Old Wolf took careful aim, fired and hit her. He then gathered some brushwood for kindling, dragged some dry branches from the forest for his fire, skinned and cleaned the doe and prepared some soup. While the soup was cooking, he speared a joint of venison on a forked branch and set it to roast gently. Soon the delicious cooking smells filled the air. The Son of Old Wolf filled his pipe with tobacco, lit it with an ember from the fire and sat down at some distance from his camp and smoked.

Darkest night had fallen, when suddenly a faint rustling sound came from the undergrowth. The Son of Old Wolf looked in the direction of the sounds but did not move from his seat. After some time, a dark figure emerged from the forest and with loud snorting sounds sniffed the air. When it came within the bright circle illuminated by the fire, the Son of Old Wolf realized it was the same beast he had seen the previous night at his home. It was a mighty Forest Ogre, covered in shaggy black fur. He had enormous shoulders, and his arms hung all the way to the ground so that he supported himself on them when he walked. He had only one leg, and a sharp horn jutted from his breast bone. He had tiny, bloodshot eyes, and he peered at everything as though he was short-sighted.

The Son of Old Wolf did not have his rifle or any other weapon with him, for he had laid them aside during his work to keep them from getting in his way. So he stayed in the shadows, hidden from the Forest Ogre.

The Forest Ogre approached the fire, sniffing at the cauldron full of soup, which he had apparently never seen before. When he saw the pieces of liver simmering in the soup, he reached into the cauldron to taste it. The boiling water scalded his hand and he roared out in pain. He probably thought some invisible enemy had bitten him, and in a rage he cast about for someone to attack. He caught sight of the cloak lying nearby and took it for a beast preparing to attack him. He pounced on it and with the horn on his chest, tore it to shreds. Then he spied the rifle leaning against the tree. He grabbed it by the barrel and bent it with his powerful arms so that it was utterly useless.

Seeing the Forest Ogre's immense strength, the Son of Old Wolf realized he could not fight him, so he decided to play for time. He remembered someone once telling him that Forest Ogres love the sound of singing. So he cleared his throat and with a quiet voice began to sing an old ballad about Mohammed, son of Hatchov. The Forest Ogre looked at the Son of Old Wolf in astonishment; his anger was calmed, and he sat down on the ground and listened closely.

The Son of Old Wolf sang right through the long song, and when he had finished, fell silent. Then the Forest Ogre sprang up again, and growling angrily, crept towards him. So the Son of Old Wolf had to keep on singing. He sang all the way

through another song, but the Forest Ogre was still not satisfied, so he had to sing again and again. His only remaining hope of escape was to lull the Forest Ogre to sleep, but for the present, the Forest Ogre was sitting listening to the song.

The venison on the fire no longer smelled fragrantly for it was smoking and starting to burn. The wind, which kept changing direction, wafted the smoke towards the Son of Old Wolf, and unable to control himself, he started to cough and could sing no more.

The Forest Ogre rose up again and howling, began to beat his chest with his fists. Then he grasped hold of a branch, swung himself up, and with a powerful leap, swooped down on the Son of Old Wolf. The Son of Old Wolf realized he could not escape into the forest. The monster feared fire, and this was his only chance. He leapt aside and dashed to the fire, putting it between him and the Forest Ogre. For some time they chased each other around the fire and more than once the Son of Old Wolf was within the reach of the monster's long arms.

The Son of Old Wolf saw no way of escape, and suddenly in his desperation he stooped down and seized his sword, then placed himself in front of a stately oak tree. The Forest Ogre let out a roar, and with short hops on his one leg, closed in on him. He stretched out his arms, crouched and with one mighty leap tried to impale the hunter to the tree with his horn. This was what the Son of Old Wolf was waiting for. Swiftly, he leapt aside, shielding himself behind the tree. The Forest Ogre struck the tree with his chest and his horn was so deeply imbedded in the trunk that he could not pull it out. The Son of Old Wolf seized his opportunity and with his sword drawn, leapt up to the beast and pierced the monster through the heart. The dying beast clasped the tree with his arms and all but tore it out by the roots. Then suddenly all his strength vanished as he died.

The Son of Old Wolf wiped the sweat from his brow and rested for a long while. In the morning he tried to tear the body from the trunk, but he did not succeed. He had to fell the tree and chop it up. Not until then could he free the monster's horn and examine the beast properly. He cut off the Forest Ogre's horn, then packed up the pieces of his cloak, picked up the bent gun and set off for home.

When he saw brother returning without any game, Happy Dog was greatly astonished. But he merely asked:

'What were you doing, brother?'

'Singing,' replied the Son of Old Wolf.

'No doubt your throat is parched,' said Happy Dog and handed him a bowl of water.

Then they ate a simple supper of gruel with cheese. After they had eaten, they lit their pipes and gazed into the fire. After some time, the Son of Old Wolf said:

'Today I forfeited my cloak and my rifle. I forfeited my sword when I discovered that my bride had left me of her own free will. I cut off the kidnapper's ear and threw the sword away. It does not matter. I shall have a new one. You will carve me a hilt for it from this bone.' And he drew the Forest Ogre's horn from his pack.

He puffed at his pipe for a while and then he added:

'You know, brother, that my name is Big Bear. From this day forth, I wish the others to know it, too.'

The Thirteenth Bullet

The mountainous countryside of Owari enjoyed a peaceful existence. The villagers felled trees and burned charcoal, which they would carry over the narrow trails to the nearest towns. Hunters were successful here, for there was an abundance of game. As the days spun out, nothing ever happened that was worth the telling.

Until suddenly, everything changed, and not a single day went by without something happening to upset the whole village. At first, fowl began to go astray, then cattle began to disappear. Even worse the villagers themselves began to fear for their safety. Often those who were confident of knowing their way did not return home from the fields at nightfall. In the morning they were found with torn limbs and mauled faces.

The villagers knew that some unknown beast was terrorizing the forest, so they organized expeditions to track it down. They spread ingenious traps, but the beast was unusually clever. It was as though it knew exactly what the villagers were doing, and purposely attacked in a different spot.

A dark, dreadful oppression lay over the whole area. No one dared to step out of his house after nightfall.

At that time, high in the mountains, there lived a lone hunter named Gompei. He was a courageous man who would stand alone against the wildest boar. He was also renowned for the accuracy of his bullets as they hit his target. When Gompei learned of the strange beast that terrorized the countryside he decided to hunt it down and free the villagers from this horror.

He wandered through the forests from morning till night, but found nothing unusual. He read the tracks of deer and wild boar; he knew where a fox had run, or a badger's trail.

Patiently he waited by the rivers where animals came to drink, but he found nothing. He no longer returned home, but spent his nights as chance would have it. Sometimes with friendly villagers, sometimes in the abandoned huts of woodcutters and charcoal burners.

He saw nothing suspicious, although it did seem that little by little he was falling prey to hallucinations. Once, he imagined that he heard sharp, malicious laughter in deserted countryside where he knew not another living soul existed. Another time he thought that his endless searching must have derranged his senses! Deep in the forest, he saw a beautiful maiden sitting by a tree spinning on a spinning wheel. A lamp hung beside her, shining in full daylight. But as soon as he drew closer, the apparition vanished.

Gompei decided that he would rest. At home his mother welcomed him and pointed to a small black cat.

'I found her in the forest, utterly abandoned. The poor thing was starving and chilled to the bone. But look how pretty she is now!'

The cat purred contentedly and nestled against her. Gompei related what had taken place in the forest, ate to his heart's content and went to bed.

The next day he rose at day-break and prepared to set off again. He wrapped up a few pancakes and stowed his bullets away in his pouch. He was carefully counting them when he had the feeling that someone was watching him intently. 'Who could be here,' he thought to himself, 'when mother is still sleeping.' He looked around and noticed that his mother's cat was watching him from her corner.

'Ah, I am beginning to see danger everywhere,' he said in relief. But something would not give him peace, so secretly, he tucked away one bullet more.

Again Gompei spent the whole day combing the forest, but he found nothing. He wandered quite far, and decided to spend the night in a hut where he often slept when he was out hunting. He was so weary that he quickly ate the pancakes he had with him, and soon fell fast asleep.

Night fell. The sky was veiled with heavy clouds, and the darkness was complete. Gompei tossed restlessly in his sleep. Suddenly he sat up with a start, wakened by a soft rustling. It sounded as though someone was creeping stealthily through the undergrowth. Quietly he jumped up, prepared his gun and drew aside the straw mat over the door.

In the dead silence of the dark night, a pair of enormous fiery eyes was silently coming closer and closer to the hut. No animal that he had ever seen had eyes such as these! Determinedly he overcame the horror within him and raised his rifle. He aimed right between those terrible eyes and fired. A metallic clash rang out. The shot had found its mark, but the eyes kept on shining. They blazed but ever brighter and drew slowly nearer. Quickly Gompei fired a second bullet and the same metallic sound rang out and again the eyes drew a little closer. Gompei fired one bullet after another and each time the same metallic sound was repeated, and after each shot the huge blazing eyes drew nearer and nearer. Otherwise, there was utter stillness and darkness around them. Not a leaf quivered in the forest. In despair Gompei fired his twelfth bullet – his last. And that one too bounced off with the same metallic sound. At that moment a terrible laughter pealed out in the darkness of the night, and Gompei froze in horror. The huge eyes were suddenly ablaze with fire – and then Gompei remembered the bullet which he had tucked away secretly. Swiftly he aimed and fired. A horrible scream rang out and the flaming eyes vanished. Utter silence set in once again.

Gompei wiped away the perspiration from his face. In that darkness there was no point in looking to see what had

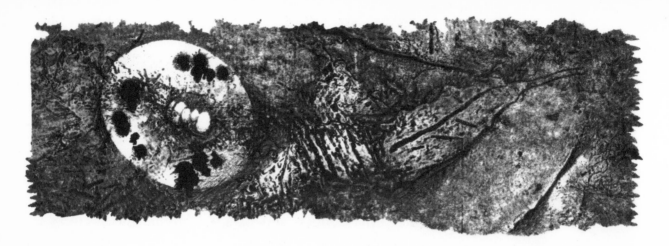

occurred. He returned to the hut and stayed on guard all
night. But all was now quiet in the forest.

Slowly the day broke. The voices of songbirds came to life
with the dawn and the forest was returning to its daylight
existence. As soon as there was light enough to see the path,
Gompei left the hut and went to examine the spot where the
eyes had shone in the night.

In the open clearing he found all twelve of his bullets, and a
little distance away, an iron lid from a rice pot. The lid was
dotted with small depressions, evidently caused by the
bullets.

'Aha, so this was what made that metallic sound,' thought
Gompei.

A bloody set of tracks led into the forest. Cautiously
Gompei followed them and in a little while, he found a
gigantic dead cat with three tails. It was Nekomata, the
ghostly cat, who had been terrorizing the whole countryside,
he said to himself, as he buried its body. Very few people had
ever seen her true likeness. Usually people encountered only
her huge, flaming eyes, which brought death in their wake.
She got control over all the ordinary cats in a region, and then
there was trouble, for she always learnt about everything
from them in advance.

Suddenly Gompei started in fright, for he remembered the
new cat that his mother had found in the forest. Nekomata
liked to take the image of a dear, good little cat and wheedle
her way into a person's home. Gompei hurried home at once,
terrified of what might have happened to his mother.

But she welcomed him as always, and only complained that
she had not been able to cook the rice properly.

'The lid for the rice pot has disappeared. I have grown so
old that I do not know where I put things any more. And that
dear little cat has disappeared too!'

56

Night
Hallucinations

In the city of Bukhara in the land of Ma-wara-an-nahr, there once lived a young shopkeeper who had the sons of princes and ministers amongst his friends. They had agreed that every week, one of them would play host to the others at a feast in his palace. Each feast was more lavish than the last; the wine flowed abundantly, the food was delicious, and beautiful slave-girls danced and sang for them to the accompaniment of lutes. When the young man's turn came, he was very distressed, for he could not imagine inviting his friends to his father's house. There, they would find none of this luxury. His father had only one slave who was his housekeeper. She was old and toothless and she sang as she cooked, accompanied by the clatter of pots and pans. It was scarcely a sound to please his rich friends.

The young man became tormented by the problem that he faced. While he was walking in the city, he met one of the sorcerers of Khorezm, who said to him:

'I know about you – how you would like to entertain your friends but you do not have the money to pay for it. Bring your friends to the abandoned summer palace behind the city cemetery, and there you will find everything that you need. I shall be your host and I shall not require anything in return until midnight. Whatever you wish for after midnight will be paid for dearly, according to my reckoning. I shall leave this ring with you as token of this agreement.'

And he drew a golden ring of rare antique design from his finger.

Astonished by all this, the young man accepted the ring and examined it, not knowing what to say. But then, when he raised his eyes to look again at the sorcerer and to answer him, there was no one there. At some distance away, a snake was slithering through the dust.

Then the young man said to himself: 'I shall take advantage of this offer, because there is nothing else I can do. If I find nothing when we go to the ruined palace, I shall tell my friends that it was only a jest, and I will arrange the feast another time. I shall pay for it by selling this beautiful ring. And if everything is as the sorcerer says I shall have to make sure that the feast ends before midnight.' Thus relieved of his worries, he set off for home.

On the appointed day when his turn came round, he waited for his friends in front of the door of his house, and led them away outside the city. As they passed by the cemetery, his friends were mystified. When they came to a beautiful park which they had never seen there before, and to a path covered with carpets, they all believed in the young man, and were assured that they were on the threshold of a lavish feast. Joyfully, they hastened forward in anticipation.

When they came to the place where ruins should have stood, they saw a host of beautifully dressed boys awaiting them. Each servant held a dish of delicacies which he offered to everyone. In the courtyard, a throng of cooks greeted them, and in the garden a sumptuous carpet had been laid, enticing them to sit down. The young men sat down, and beautiful Turkish girls brought them refreshments. One delicious delicacy followed another; precious wines flowed, sweet music and singing dispelled all gloom, and for every tired head a soft repose was found. Everyone marvelled at the exquisite food and drink; at the beauty of the slave-girls, and at the costliness and luxury of the entire feast, and with one accord they proclaimed that the young man had distinguished himself over and above them all, and they acclaimed him king of their company.

The evening passed in delightful amusements. Countless candles and torches kept the darkness at bay, and the food did not dwindle, but grew more plentiful. No one, except the young man, gave a thought to the approaching midnight hour. Fear welled up in him, and more than once he tried to run away, but each time his friends caught him by the hand and cried out:

'You are our king. You must not desert your throne among us!'

Soon all the company were heavy-eyed from the wines which they had been drinking, and one after another they tottered from the carpet to find a place to sleep on the soft grass. The young man made use of his opportunity and stole away from the garden, intending to escape back to the city. But he ran away in the wrong direction and he strayed into a region which he did not know.

When at last in despair he was about to lie down in some wormwood to sleep, he caught sight of a hut where a light was still burning. He walked to the house and called to the householders. An old man and an old woman came out, they welcomed him and took pity on him, saying:

'How did you get into this region? Why, do you not know that it is full of demons?'

The young man related everything that had happened to him and they declared:

'You are lucky that you found us, and did not fall into the hands of the sorcerer who rules over all the demons in this region. He would surely have devoured you, for your life is the wage exacted by that sorcerer.'

They showed the young man to a simple bed and exhausted he fell asleep. Suddenly a noise awakened him, and when he looked up, he saw the old man and the old woman sharpening long knives and preparing to cut his throat. He let out a shriek and dashed out of the hut and fled as fast as his legs would carry him. The old man and woman ran in pursuit, brandishing the knives.

They were just about to catch up with him, tearing along on legs that had suddenly grown young, when the young man caught sight of a saddled horse grazing in a field. He leapt up on it and urged it on with his heels. The horse galloped like the wind, and headed further into the desert. It galloped up a hill, pushed itself off, and flew into the air. It was more than a few paces from the ground when a flame flashed out of its mouth and it turned into a terrifying dragon.

It flew up and down, and turning its hideous head, it inspected the young man greedily. The young man took advantage of a moment when they were closest to the ground, slid down the spine of the dragon and fell into some bushes. In the fall, he broke his leg and dislocated his jawbone, so that he could neither stand nor call out. He gazed at the flickering stars, waiting for the next monster to snatch him.

Then in the distance he heard the sound of quiet singing and someone's footfalls. In a little while, a dervish with a wise expression and a kindly smile appeared. When he saw the young man and discovered what condition he was in, he knelt down beside him like a trained doctor, straightened his jawbone and mended his leg. Then he asked the young man who he was and what he was doing there. The young man told him all about the sorcerer and about the feast; he told of the old man and the old woman and the terrible horse. And the dervish replied:

'You are indeed lucky that I found you here. No doubt they were all demons which the sorcerer has under his command. If I had not chanced to pass by, they would have swooped down and devoured you. But now you are safe. Not far from here lives an acquaintance of mine who will give you shelter until the morning and will send someone to the city with you, for you have strayed so far, that you would not find the way alone.'

And together they journied on until they came to a house in the middle of a garden, where an old man lived with his daughters. The dervish described the events of the past night and the old man agreed to let the young man stay with him for the remainder of the night and to send a servant with him to the city in the morning. But he suggested that the young man should sleep in the tent that stood in the garden, for he would not like to see him spending the night under the same roof as his daughters. The young man thanked him and went out to the tent at once, to rest after all the hardships he had suffered.

He had not slept long, though, when he heard someone making their way towards him. He asked who it was, and beheld a maiden with a face like the moon and lips of coral. The young man was shy and hid from the maiden, but she said to him:

'Come with me and my sisters out into the park and let us amuse ourselves, for we live here in the desert all alone, and no one comes to visit us except that dervish. Father is very strict and does not allow us to meet anyone else. If you do not come, I shall call him and tell him that you are a cunning robber and that you tried to rob him of his riches, and he will drive you out into the desert.'

The young man feared nothing more than he feared the desert and so he obeyed the maiden and went out of the tent. He found a carpet spread out, and three beautiful maidens such as the world had never seen, were sitting there and they invited him into their circle. Partly out of fear and partly out of high spirits, the young man sat down among the maidens and began to talk to them. When the merriment was at its height, the maidens proposed that each of them would hide in a different place in the garden and he would look for them. And they ran off and hid in different directions. The young man, full of laughter and good cheer and now feeling no fear at all, began to search for them in the garden, and they lured him on and on until they came to the most remote corner. There the young man saw the most beautiful of the maidens hidden amongst the branches of a tree. He called out to her, and she began to lure him towards her. As he stepped up to her, she put her head on his shoulder and turned her lips to him. Believing that no danger threatened him, the young man kissed her. But hardly had he kissed her, when the maiden said:

'It is long after midnight. You wanted a night's lodging with the old man and woman, then you rode on a horse which did not belong to you, and now you desire a honey-lipped beauty. The time has come for you to settle your account.'

And she was transformed into a hideous demon which sank its teeth into his lips and buried its claws in his chest. The garden, the house and the tent all vanished, and the young man found himself alone with the demon in the middle of the desert under a bare tree on which vultures sat. He screamed out in horror, freed himself from the clutches of the demon and ran away.

'You will run far; I have my pledge with you,' the demon roared after him in a terrible voice.

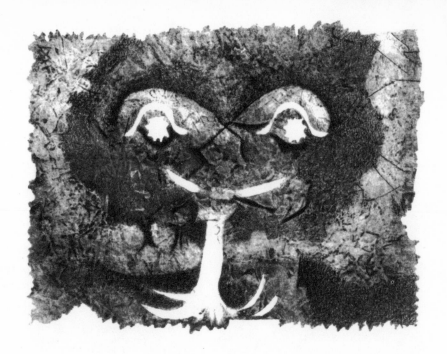

The young man remembered the ring which he had received from the sorcerer. He reached into his bosom where he had hidden it, pulled it out and flung it away in a high curve. All at once he saw the ring change into a snake which slithered in the dust.

He ran on with all his strength until daybreak. And when the day dawned, he saw that he was on the edge of the cemetery and that the minarets of the city were in sight. As he walked among the graves, he found all the rest of the young men sleeping comfortably there, and when he woke them, they knew nothing except how very much they had had to drink.

From that day on, the young man avoided his friends. He attended to his shop, and when the opportunity came, he departed from the region with a caravan, never to return.

A Conversation by the Charcoal Heaps

Many strange sounds break the silence of the woods at night, the snapping of twigs under the footfall of animals, the beating of wings at night, the hooting of owls, the screeching of bats and the murmur of the wind in the trees. It is as though the forest itself was speaking to its inhabitants. But very few people understand the secret language of the forest at night. Those who occasionally spend a night in the dark forest cannot distinguish between an animal's footstep and the sound of a bird's wings, and their hearing is deadened by their fear of unknown dangers. While those who live in the forest all the time are too accustomed to its whispering. They see behind every rustling or faint footfall a branch lifted by a breath of wind or an animal on the prowl, and they listen no more. Therefore, it only rarely happens that a person meets one of the ghostly beings that make their home hidden in the forest.

Deep in the forests on the Haguro mountains, where the bamboo stops growing and slender cryptomeria tower above the pines, a young girl named Otama once experienced such an encounter. Her father was a charcoal burner; from spring to autumn he burned charcoal in the forest and only now and then did he set off down into the village with a load of charcoal for sale. Otama lived with her father throughout the summer in a small hut in a clearing; she cooked for him, took care of him and helped him mind the charcoal.

One day, her father went to the village with a load of charcoal and left Otama alone in the forest. She was not frightened, for she was accustomed to the forest and she was a courageous girl. Only in the evening when it had grown dark and her father still had not returned, did she feel a little uneasy. But then she sat down by the fire in the hut, waiting

with supper ready for her father, and passed the time
pleasantly in thought.

Outside all was quiet, except from time to time, above the
crackling of the fire, a violent rustling could be heard. Oh, it is
nothing but the wind, she reassured herself, and she kept on
waiting until she began to feel sleepy. For a while she resisted
sleep, then she dozed a little, and when the strange rustling
woke her again, she decided that she would prepare her bed.
And when her father still did not come, she said to herself that
she would wait no more.

She was preparing for bed, when suddenly the mat hanging
over the door of the hut curled aside a little and then fell back.
It was as though someone wanted to look inside and then had
changed his mind. The girl was frightened; but then she told
herself that it had probably been a gust of wind. After a little
while, the mat moved again, and this time a faint red glow
could be seen coming from outside the hut. One of the
charcoal heaps has cracked, Otama thought to herself. I must
go outside and wet it down.

She got up and went outside. Then she saw that the light
was not coming from a cracked charcoal heap, as she had
thought, but from the tips of the trees at the edge of the
clearing. Before she could decide what it was, a strange faintly
glowing figure with wings on its back swooped down from
the trees. When the apparition came closer, she saw that it was

a winged man with a large head. His face glowed red and he had a long, stout nose.

It was a tengu, a spirit of the forest. He slowly moved closer to the girl, examining her eagerly. She was so frightened that she could not move, and she simply waited for the tengu to either tear her to pieces or to carry her far away to his nest deep in the forest.

Suddenly the tengu stopped, put his hands on his hips, laughed in a croaking voice and said:

'So you think that I shall tear you to pieces or carry you away. I shall have to give it further thought.'

Then he walked around the girl, first from one side, then from the other, and all the time his glittering eyes were fastened upon her. It flashed through her mind that perhaps she could run away, but just then the tengu laughed again:

'Surely you do not want to run away from me? You would never succeed. Watch!' He rose into the air and swiftly flew here and there above the clearing a few times, until the tips of the trees rustled.

He stopped in front of the girl and examined her again with the same absorption. Now he will start to tear me apart, she thought in terror, and the tengu said:

'No I shall not tear you apart, that would be a pity. You are so pretty; you have such a tiny nose, and I like you. I should prefer to take you in one piece. I will carry you off to my bird-like children; they will love having such a pretty toy.'

So that huge nose grew out of a beak, thought Otama, and she was less frightened, for it seemed quite amusing. And the tengu continued:

'You see, you did not know that young tengus look like birds. Only an adult tengu has such a fine nose as mine.'

Otama almost laughed, and said to herself that this tengu was not terrifying after all, and that she might possibly be able to outwit him. But the tengu went on:

'You people think you are so clever, and in fact you do not know the half of it. And you would like to outwit me! I like that, in fact, I am looking forward to it. You are so pretty and so brave, that I shall not tear you to pieces nor shall I carry you off, even though I could.

'We shall play a game together. Perhaps you have noticed that I always guess what you are thinking. And it is no coincidence, as you thought just now, but one of the most ordinary skills of a tengu! This will be our game: you will think about whatever you like, and I shall guess it. If I do not guess every time, you win and I shall no longer have any

power over you. But if you lose, you are mine, and I shall carry you away and you will never return again!'

It was evident that the tengu was looking forward to displaying his skill to the girl. He preened himself, reddened even more, and in his excitement the tiny feathers on his wings quivered.

Otama saw that the tengu meant it seriously and that she had to accept his terms. She was quite glad that there was some hope left after all, and she sat down on a log in front of the hut and watched the tengu.

'Let us begin,' said the tengu.

'You are thinking that such a creature, who is neither human nor animal, cannot know everything, and you plan to surprise me somehow.'

'You are thinking that your father cannot be far away by now and that he will drive me away.'

'You are thinking that you will have to think of something else.'

'You are thinking that your friend Kinu from the village has a wart on her left elbow.'

'You are thinking that she is fond of the neighbour's son Goro, and that she has told no one about it but you.'

'You are thinking that at home you have a black lacquer box from your grandmother and in that box there is a hair–ribbon and that ribbon is all in knots, for you tangled it and forgot to untie it.'

The tengu spoke faster and faster, his eyes blazed brighter and brighter and little by little he was drawing closer to the girl.

'You are thinking that you do not know what to think any more so that I will not guess it.'

'You are thinking that you have no hope of winning any more.'

By now he was quite near and he was reaching out towards her.

'You are thinking that now I shall pounce on you.'

'You are thinking that you cannot go on any more.'

Just then the girl was overcome with such terror and faintness that she fell unconscious to the ground. As she was falling, her hand brushed against a pile of sticks, and one of them bounced up and struck the tengu on the nose.

The tengu started, looked at the girl in amazement, and then shook his head, bewildered.

'Now that I did not expect. Why, I always guess what a person is thinking and so I know what he will do. But never

before have I seen someone do something before the thought enters his mind. It appears that people are not so foolish after all!'

He pondered on the matter for some time, staring at Otama, and when the girl regained consciousness and stood up, he said to her quite gently:

'You are an unusually clever girl and I like you all the more. But since I lost the contest, I shall go away without you.'

But somehow he could not bring himself to leave. He lingered on, as though he were trying to make up his mind about something. Otama did not know what this meant and so she remained apprehensive. Finally the tengu made up his mind, and he spoke out almost ceremoniously:

'As I have already said, you are truly an exceptional girl and so you deserve something special. I have decided to reveal a little bit of tengu knowledge to you, so you will have a keepsake of our meeting. Listen carefully. When we tengus are learning to guess what a person is thinking, we begin our training by watching the other's face closely. For you see, thoughts are visible on everyone's face. But you will come to know them only when you have learned to take on precisely the same expression as the other person. Then you will think what he is thinking. That is the simplest method for the most ordinary thoughts, but for a human being it is quite enough. Try it, and you will see that it will come in useful.'

When the tengu finished speaking, he looked regretfully at Otama once more, waved his wings and added: 'Your father is coming.' Then he rose into the air and disappeared among the tips of the trees.

The branches of the trees were still quivering a little when footsteps could be heard and the old coal burner came running into the clearing, and still running, he called out:

'Otama, are you there? Why, that was a tengu! Did he harm you?'

'No, daddy, he only frightened me a little, but in the end he was quite nice.'

Her father took her by the hand and they went together into the hut.

'How glad I am that nothing happened to you! I was held up a little in the village and the whole way back I reproached myself for leaving you here all alone so late into the night.'

During supper Otama was silent and from time to time she fastened her eyes intently on her father's face.

The Festival
of Lights

Many years ago, a monk named Denkai began to travel. He wandered from place to place; slept here and there and in the end became an itinerant monk who roamed over all the Japanese empire.

That year, as he was returning from a pilgrimage in the northern provinces to the emperor's city of Kyoto, he decided to finally visit the famous Festival of Lights which was celebrated in the Lotus Temple, in the nearby city of Nara. He had often heard both monks and laymen describe the brilliant torch-light procession, the beautiful singing of the monks and the exalting midnight ceremony, but in all the long years of his wandering, he had never succeeded in reaching the Lotus Temple on the day of the festival. Something always occurred that prevented him reaching the festival as though chance willed him not to go. He found nothing strange in this, for he liked to change his destination according to his mood of the moment, like a ship on the waves of the high seas. But this time, he said to himself, he would not let the festival pass him by. He would allow nothing to detract him from arriving at the Lotus Temple.

Everything went well on his journey. His legs were strong, although he was no longer in the springtime of his youth, and in the evening he always found a night's lodging and hospitality in a monastery or with kind people. And so he happily reached two days' journey from his destination, three days before the festival.

This time I shall take part in the festival, Denkai congratulated himself, as he strode across a deserted valley under the Nagano pass. The path meandered through a grassy plain and the sun was slowly sinking in the west. Denkai began to wonder where he would spend the coming night and

he searched the horizon for signs of a village. He noticed a
large house standing by itself at the end of the valley. As he
came closer, he discovered that it was not a house, but a large
temple with a long, covered staircase leading up to it from the
foot of the hill. Denkai rejoiced for surely he would find
shelter and a little food here.

He set off in the direction of the temple. As he approached
it, he found it strange that he had not seen a living person near
it. Nothing stirred in the stillness of the coming night. When
he reached the gate at the foot of the hill, he marvelled at how
closely the temple resembled the Lotus Temple in the city of
Nara. Then he discovered that the temple had been long
abandoned. The roof above the portal had caved in; the
wooden posts were askew, the stone steps were covered with
moss and grass grew in the chinks between the stones. Denkai
was dismayed, but because it was already evening, he decided
to spend the night in the temple, as at least he would have a
roof over his head. He went up the stairs and entered the main
hall. It was empty, warmed by the sun, and smelled of old
wood and incense.

In the last rays of the setting sun, Denkai found himself a
corner with a view over the countryside. He settled down
comfortably and began to wonder why this fine temple was
falling into disrepair, and why it was not used by anyone.
Thus he sat and thought about the temple and about his
travels and quietly dozed as evening became night.

Meanwhile a cool wind blew up from the mountains.
Denkai shivered, drew his black robe closer around his body
and tucked his hands into his sleeves. Looking out over the
valley, he noticed a glare above the pass in the distance. Before
long, a bright light swung over the horizon, slipped down into

the valley and was moving in the direction of the temple. After a while the mysterious light divided into a great many tiny lights and he could see the throng of lights drawing across the valley.

It is most strange, Denkai thought, that in all my travels no one has told me about this temple nor that some kind of nocturnal ceremony takes place here. What is more, there are so many lights that it must be a great celebration. Before it occurred to him that the procession was moving extraordinarily quickly; faster than men could run, the lights were already at the foot of the hill, at the gates of the temple.

The stream of lights rushed through the gates and moved up the staircase. But there was no sound of footsteps or voices, only a sort of rustling, like unintelligible distant whispering.

Denkai crouched in his corner, hardly breathing, and waited to see what would happen. Presently the doors flew open, the main hall suddenly blazed with light, and a multitude of strange beings rushed headlong into the room. They were neither human beings nor animals, but rather like sections of human and animal bodies that had joined together by chance.

Denkai forgot to be frightened, and he stared at the human bodies with buffalo or horse's heads, a cat's body with the face of a young girl, a rooster with the shaven head of a monk, and a legless figure with a big head on an enormously long snake's neck which stretched and writhed as the head peered into every corner of the hall. Then he saw human forms amongst them with missing or added body parts; a woman with one eye in the centre of her face and lips on her forehead, a man with three noses and one large ear on his chest, and a thin legless creature with long arms that reached all the way down to the ground and a woman's and man's head on one neck. There were also human limbs moving about; two legs without a body, hands which would clasp one another and separate, and a head peering out of a wicker basket. A translucent mist swirled along the floor. Every so often it changed its shape, and with every movement a shining eye, a long nose, flapping ears or a row of sharp teeth would appear and then disappear again.

The apparitions made no sound and a faint eerie light glowed around them. Soon the hall was full, until last of all, the enormous figure of a demon, who towered all the way to the ceiling, appeared in the doorway. He was black, so black that he gleamed; on his head were three blunt horns, and a huge nose fell to his chin. His fingers were so thick that they stood apart. He wore a tiger skin around his mighty stomach, and a long furry tail could be seen beneath it.

The demon sat down at the top of the hall, while the phantoms remained standing respectfully, apparently waiting for his command. The demon looked at them, rolled his eyes and then spoke in a deep voice:

'For the present, we have reached the goal of our wandering on this earth. I am happy to see you all together. Before we go on our ways again, I should like to speak to you. Be seated.'

The phantoms sat down on the floor one after the other. They squirmed and jostled and presently all were quietly seated. Only a long thin creature with just half a body and one leg remained standing in the centre of the hall.

'I told you all to sit down,' the demon frowned. 'Why are you standing, One-legged?'

The one-legged creature looked discontentedly to the right and to the left and replied indignantly: 'How can I sit down when there is no room for me?'

For a moment there was silence, until the head on the snake's neck stretched out and hissed: 'There is someone here who does not belong among us!'

Then all the phantoms began to look around the hall, until they spotted Denkai crouching in the corner, quaking with terror. For a long while that multitude of terrible eyes was focused upon him, until at last the huge demon spoke again:

'So there is no room for you? Then I shall make room for you.' And he raised his enormous hand and slowly stretched it out toward Denkai. When the monk saw that open palm with the thick fingers above him, he crouched down even more, but it was no use. The enormous hand snatched him by the collar, lifted him high into the air, thrust him out the window and bore him all the way down to the gate of the temple. The terrified Denkai supported himself against the stone steps and for a while he could not move. When nothing more happened, and the pale light in the temple went out, the monk, exhausted from his experiences, fell asleep.

In the morning the sun shone and Denkai woke up. He stretched, and then suddenly remembered what had happened during the night. He shook his head at his peculiar dream, and began to get ready to continue his journey. Then he noticed that the sun was shining too brightly. He started, looked around and discovered that he was not even sitting at the gates of the temple. The temple had vanished. Denkai rubbed his eyes and looked around once again. But he saw

75

neither the valley nor even the pass on the horizon. He was in a completely different, unknown region. He was sitting in an arid plain, as flat as the palm of his hand, and in the distance through a misty haze loomed high mountains and on the other side stretched the endless expanse of the sea.

Denkai was utterly bewildered and he did not know what to do. The sun burned more and more; the hot air above the plain began to shimmer and nowhere in that flat expanse was there shade. Then in the distance he saw that something was moving along the shore. A group of figures was coming closer. He was unable to make them out against the sun. He caught sight of something like a horse's head, then something high and square, and apprehensively he waited for it to come closer. He heaved a sigh of relief when he realized that it was a group of horses loaded with packs, driven by merchants. He went forward to meet them, and after he had exchanged greetings, he asked cautiously:

'Forgive me for asking such an unseemly question, but I have somehow strayed here accidently and I should like to know where I am.'

One of the merchants laughed:

'That is a strange question! How could you wander astray, here, on the plain of Hyuga? You probably meditated too deeply, or perhaps your memory no longer serves you well?'

How is that possible, Denkai thought, why the plain of Hyuga is far to the south, on the island of Kyushu, and that is some five hundred miles from the Nagano pass, maybe even more!

'Our monk is surprised,' the merchant remarked to the others. 'He is probably hungry. Give him something to eat and drink. But then we must hurry, for we must arrive at the port shortly after noon.' Then he turned to Denkai: 'If you continue north following the shore as we do, you will also arrive there before evening,' he told him.

Denkai thanked him for his hospitality and then walked for a while at the rear of the group. But the merchants were in a hurry, and so the monk lagged behind more and more and until the horses and people disappeared in the hot haze and he was alone once more on the desert plain.

He walked and walked, the sun blazed, the calm sea lapped the beach. As he walked, his thoughts kept returning to the mysterious way he had come to this place. I have some unexpected travelling before me, he said to himself, but no matter, although I have never been in the south before, I am sure to find a monastery here. I am ill-fated, he thought, for once again I shall not see the Festival of Lights in the Lotus Temple. I could never travel such a distance in three days. And it would be unseemly for an itinerant monk to hurry somewhere, when his ultimate destination, salvation or damnation, is the same distance from all the corners of the earth. With this reflection, he chased away his regret and set his mind at rest. He stopped wondering whether the mysterious experience of the previous night had perhaps not been a punishment for some wrong-doing long ago in one of his previous lives. He stepped forth again at his tranquil pilgrim's pace and walked on and on by the sea.

It was afternoon and Denkai was tired, when his steps led him to a shallow bay. In it, he saw a boat lying on the shore. He found it strange; for how did a boat get there, when there was no human dwelling for miles around. But when he came closer, he saw that it was a wreck dried out by the sun. Either the sea had cast it forth, or else it had been pulled ashore by people who intended to repair it, and then changed their mind. The main thing is that I can rest here for a while in the shade, said Denkai to himself contentedly, and he stepped through the torn side into the boat and sat down on an exposed rib. He propped his head in his hands, rested his elbows on his knees and gazed at the sparkling bay until he was lulled into sleep.

A sudden jolt woke him, and, at the same time, he felt a cool gust of wind. He discovered that it was night, and he heard waves striking the boat. He was afraid that the high tide had caught him unawares, when suddenly he noticed that the sails were spread and that the ship was under sail. I am having another strange dream, he thought, and then he felt that he was not alone in the boat. He could see something moving in the stern, and when he looked closer, he saw three black figures moving against the starry sky. He looked to the bow and saw a small group of warriors in full armour, with spears and longbows, standing motionless and silently gazing out over the sea.

'Helmsman, you are piloting the boat badly today,' a harsh voice rang out from the bow. 'It will be your fault if we are delayed.'

No one replied, only the sails swelled even more. After a moment the voice came from the bow once again, and it sounded even stricter:

'I shall punish all of you, at the sails and at the helm, you are idlers and because of you we shall lose the battle.'

Then from the stern another voice replied:

'It is not our fault, sir, the ship is heavy and is listing to starboard.'

Denkai was following the dispute between the commander and the helmsman with interest, and he started when something moved right next to him in the bottom of the boat. He heard a groaning sound, and slowly the black figure of a warrior whose chest was pierced with arrows stood up. The figure pointed at the monk and said:

'Here is the guilty one. He is heavy and does not belong among us.'

The ghost warriors fell silent, but then the commander cried out:

'Yet another interloper from the transient world! Out with him, he must not delay us. Set him down on the island of Awaji, and then we must set sail for the shores of the marshalling ground at once, for day will soon be dawning.'

'Sir,' said the helmsman urgently. 'The sky is lightening in the east and the marshalling grounds are far away. We cannot take this monk to the island of Awaji and reach the grounds before dawn. Let us leave him on that rock over there. No harm will come to him, for the sea is calm and it is not far from the shore.'

The commander agreed and in a moment Denkai felt himself falling and before he knew what was happening he was standing on firm ground. There was no trace of the boat or the knights.

When Denkai recovered from his fright, day was slowly dawning and a light mist was rising from the ground. After a moment he discovered that he was standing on a large rock surrounded by sea. It was utterly calm, and rippled gently in tiny wavelets under the coils of morning mist. Denkai sat down on the rock carefully and gazed into the mist and reflected on his peculiar experiences of the night. The mist was gradually clearing and he could see land not far away, and on the shore he saw a boat. Then he saw trees, and suddenly figures emerged from amongst them, moving quietly along the shore. The first figure stopped, pointed in Denkai's direction and they all turned and stood still. Then a puff of morning wind wafted away the remaining mist and it turned out that the black figures were monks, and behind the trees rose the roof of a temple.

Denkai waved to the monks joyfully. They untied the boat and ferried him to the shore. There Denkai learned that he was in the lake adjoining the Temple of the Heavenly Dragon in Kyoto. He rejoiced that he had returned to the region in which he had originally been travelling, for it seemed that he could still arrive in time for the Festival of Lights in the Lotus Temple in the nearby city of Nara.

And so he set off on his journey without delay, and if his path was not crossed by spirits once again, perhaps he even managed to arrive there.

Unhappy
Mrs Lee

Kuo Yu lived in his native town of I in the province of Shan-tung quite contentedly. Though it is true that he earned his living in all sorts of ways, he was usually to be found hanging about the market-place, one time running as an errand-boy with a message, another time helping to carry a heavy delivery into a shop. He always managed to earn a handful of coins for rice and tea, and sometimes he even had enough left over for something extra.

One day he sat drinking with his friends in the inn The Round Jug. They talked of many things and Kuo became excited at the many strange and incredible things that there are in this world. Time ran on and the beating of the drums was announcing the beginning of the third night watch when the revellers finally said their farewells and went home.

Kuo returned alone. A full moon shone above the hushed narrow streets of the town, creating a sharp contrast between the bright places and the sombre shadows. As Kuo walked along the lane leading to the temple, he saw a figure emerge from the temple and stride down the centre of the brightly illuminated lane. It approached lightly and soundlessly, as if driven by the wind, although not a leaf stirred.

Kuo stopped and thought seriously: Whoever could it be, so late at night?

He stepped back into the dark shadows and waited for the figure to come closer. It was evidently a woman. And probably a lady, thought Kuo judging by her clothes. She was tall and slender, dressed in a loose robe with a bluish-green jacket. She strode lightly without any visible movement of her legs. Dark eyes stared from a face so chalk-white that it was ghostly pale.

'That lady looks completely deranged,' Kuo said to

himself. 'Wandering about in the night without her maid. I must find out more about this!'

The woman was moving quickly, and Kuo increased his pace and cautiously followed her. The woman moved faster and faster and suddenly she disappeared into a side alley. Kuo had some difficulty in catching up with her. He just caught sight of her entering a house, but he was not sure which, for no door had opened anywhere, nor had there been the slightest creaking sound. Kuo crept carefully from house to house, trying to find some way in.

'Surely one of them must be open! Otherwise, what could have become of her?'

Finally at the end of the alley he found a gate which, although not open, was so shabby that he could easily squeeze through, and he found himself standing in a small courtyard. A feeble light shone in a window to the right of the gate. Kuo stole carefully to the window and peered into the room.

A woman sat by a small oil lamp, sighing sorrowfully.

'Why, that is Mrs Lee,' Kuo said to himself. 'She is lonely, for just after her wedding, her husband went away on a long journey and he has not returned yet. She is grieved at what could possibly have happened to him.'

Kuo felt ashamed to be looking into a stranger's household, and he was about to leave, when he caught sight of the strange woman in the room. She stood there, mute and motionless.

Whatever did those two women have in common? Kuo asked himself. He crouched quietly at the window and anxiously watched.

At first, nothing happened. The strange lady stood in the corner of the room; Mrs Lee stared into the emptiness above the dying lamp, and from time to time she heaved a deep sigh.

After some time, the strange lady stepped soundlessly forward. Her pale white face was stark and rigid; her dark eyes, glowing evilly, were fastened on Mrs Lee. Slowly, she drew a rope from her loose sleeve. Then she tied it into a noose and with her eyes fixed on Mrs Lee, moved even closer to her and raised the rope high into the air.

Kuo caught his breath, and his drunkenness fell from him like a flash.

Surely that woman does not intend to strangle poor Mrs Lee? But before he had time to make up his mind about anything at all, the strange lady tossed the rope over a beam, tightened the noose and slowly slipped it over her own head.

Mrs Lee sighed so deeply that the little flame of the lamp flickered, and she continued to stare into space.

The strange lady withdrew her head from the noose, pulled the rope down from the beam and stepped one pace closer to Mrs Lee. Her eyes actually blazed, and she stared at her more and more intently. Then she slowly reached her hands out to her, holding the rope, and she tied a noose. With a soundless, easy motion, she tossed the rope over the beam, fixed the noose and slipped her head through it. While she was doing this, her evil gaze never left Mrs Lee for an instant.

Whatever is that woman doing? thought Kuo in astonishment. I shall not leave here until I find out what is behind all this.

Meanwhile, the woman, whose face remained rigid and inscrutable, patiently and without a sound repeated her actions several times in succession. Mrs Lee sighed more and more heartbreakingly, until finally she began to weep softly. Then she stood up slowly and, as if in a dream, she stepped towards the lady, and hesitantly reached out her hand to her. Without changing her expression, the lady handed her the rope. Mrs Lee took it and tossed the rope over a beam, and with a deep, melancholy sigh, laid her head in the noose. The silent lady made no move, and stared at her intently. Mrs Lee was just on the point of tightening the noose when she brushed against the table and knocked over the teapot, which shattered on the floor. The loud crash broke the silence and Mrs Lee started, shook her head and looked about, as though waking from sleep.

The strange lady's face twitched with fury. Quickly she coiled up the rope and withdrew into a corner of the room.

Mrs Lee revived the light of the fading lamp and swept up the pieces of the broken teapot. Then she sat down once again at the table and began to stare into space. Some time later, the silent lady left her corner, pulled the rope from her sleeve and showed it to Mrs Lee. Then she threw it over the beam and laid her head in the noose. Again and again she repeated these same movements, her eyes never leaving Mrs Lee.

After some time, Mrs Lee rose once again like a sleep-walker, reached out her hands and took the rope from her. She threw it over a beam and resignedly laid her head in the noose. In that instant the evil eyes in the white face blazed even brighter.

'Help! Why this is murder!' Kuo could no longer bear to remain silent and he hammered on the window.

Mrs Lee awoke from her trance and looked about herself in a daze to see what was happening.

Confusion broke out in the neighbourhood. People came

running out of their houses, asking what was happening. When they saw Kuo staring into a strange window and battering on the window and walls, they lost their tempers.

'That Kuo does not know when to stop drinking. When he gets drunk he cannot find his way home and then he causes a disturbance in other people's courtyards!'

'Hurry and run home, or we shall call the guard on you!'

But Kuo paid no attention to what was going on around him. He kept his eyes riveted on the strange lady. At first she had drawn back into the corner as before, but now when such an outcry had broken out, she darted away. Kuo sprang after her and tried to catch her, but he only succeeded in wrenching the rope away from her. The lady vanished.

Kuo quickly wound the rope around his arm and prepared to tell the infuriated people what he had just witnessed. But no one let him get a word in edgeways. They shouted at him, telling him not to wake them with his drunken bawling. Finally Kuo waved his hand, and taking offence, he walked away.

The people slowly returned to their homes, and the neighbourhood fell silent once again. Kuo walked and pondered on what could possibly have been going on. But he had scarcely turned the corner, when suddenly from out of the dark shadows, the figure of that strange lady emerged. Her white face shone in the light of the moon like a mask. She stepped toward him and spoke to him in a low, almost soundless voice.

'Give me back my rope.'

When he heard that eerie voice, Kuo started in fright, but he recovered at once.

'I shall give you no rope. What sort of idea is that – forcing a poor woman to hang herself.'

The strange lady entreated, implored and then again commanded imperiously for him to give her back the rope. She tried to prove to him that she was not to blame. She herself had died a violent death and now she wandered in the land of ghosts. Until she found a substitute for herself, she could not return to the cycle of life and be reborn as a new being. Only in that way could she atone for her sins of the past and set out on the road to redemption. Without that rope, however, she would not find a substitute and would wander as a ghost forever.

Kuo remained unwavering.

'I shall give you back the rope, and you will force poor Mrs Lee to hang herself. That is out of the question. You will no doubt talk them into changing their minds about you in the underworld, and waiving the substitute.'

When she did not get her way peacefully, the ghost suddenly pounced on him and tried to tear the rope away from him. But he had it wound about his arm and he gripped the end tightly in his hand. The woman jerked on the rope with all her strength, and Kuo flailed about with his arms, his hands closed into fists, he kicked and ran away from the white lady screaming at the top of his voice that he would give her nothing. His shouts attracted the neighbours once again, who watched his performance in astonishment. They all agreed that they had never seen Kuo so drunk before. He was making the most terrible noise.

Meanwhile, the white lady succeeded in seizing the end of the rope and she began to tug it from Kuo's arm. He thrashed about in such a frenzy that he banged his nose against a wall, and blood spurted out and splashed the white lady's dress. In that instant, both she and the rope vanished.

Kuo looked about in confusion, but he saw only the faces of his neighbours, some enraged, some convulsed in laughter. 'What are you doing, raising such a storm, go on home,' they chided him one after the other. One of his friends was also among them, and he took Kuo home. Kuo did not speak another word and exhausted, he fell asleep.

When he awoke in the morning, he was not at all sure whether he had not in fact drunk a little more than he was accustomed to at The Round Jug, and whether it had not all been just a drunken hallucination. But then he noticed that on his left arm, where the rope had been wound, a dark red mark as if from a burn had appeared. The wound healed very slowly, and after many years he still had a clearly perceptible scar there.

The Horse
from the Sea

A young boy sat on the grassy slope and looked out over the sea. Evening was drawing near. The sea was a greyish green, it murmured softly and rolled in long, gentle waves.

The lad had been restless since morning. He had quarrelled with everyone and found fault with everything. All afternoon he rambled along the water's edge, and finally he sat down on the grass of the slope, his chin propped in his hands, and gazed out at the friendly sea.

The sun was slowly sinking behind the distant clouds, and mist began to rise like smoke from the surface of the sea. It

was grey and white, it thickened into wreathes, ringlets and fleecy knots, then merged softly like a mass of velvety curls and slowly flowed out over the darkening water.

A wide wedge of mist drifted silently to the shore and hid the tiny wavelets lapping on the sand among the pebbles and sparse grass. Then the mist in that spot thickened even more, reared up, and suddenly from out of the sea a large grey horse veiled in wet white fleece stepped silently to the shore.

The horse shook his flowing mane until the mist flew off in streams, took several long paces along the shore and stopped. Then he tossed his head, and again without the slightest sound, broke into a gallop across the grassy slope. And with long bounds, he vanished over the round green hillocks above the water's edge.

The boy watched every movement of the wondrous horse intensely. What a beautiful horse! If only I had such a horse, I would jump up on him and ride off somewhere far away, he thought, and his eyes shone.

The mist thinned again, and after a while a man appeared walking along the shore. He strolled slowly, with leisurely steps, his hands clasped behind his back. At times he would stop and look about him, as though he had nothing to do and had come out for a walk. He came closer and closer, and when he came to the boy, he stopped in front of him. He was dressed in black. He was hatless and had long, fair hair which hung to his shoulders. His face was thin and elongated with large, grey eyes.

'Are you not lonely sitting there all by yourself?' the man asked the boy.

'Sir, did you see that horse?' the boy answered with a question of his own, and stared at the round hillocks above the bank. 'What a beautiful horse! He had such a magnificent grey mane, and he galloped over there to those hills.'

'I think you should return home, it will be dark soon.'

'If I had a horse like that, I would jump up on him. He would play up for a moment, then he would turn and gallop like the wind.'

'Would you not be afraid?'

'I would hold on to him, and I would say to him, run, little horse, and I would ride somewhere far away.'

'But what if he threw you?'

'My horse would never throw me.'

'Then it is a pity that you do not have a horse. But I have an idea, I will at least give you a ride as though you were on a horse. Come, jump up on me.'

The man smiled, leaned over, gave the boy his hand and sat him astride on his shoulders. Then he jumped up, whirled about and broke into a run along the shore, leaping and bounding. In a little while he turned around and ran back again.

The man shook his head until his long fair hair flew in the wind. The boy laughed, he was no longer in the least bit sulky, and he cried out: 'Run little horse, let us go somewhere far away.' From that height he looked out over the green hillocks above the seashore and over the purling sea where swirls of mist were rolling in from the ocean.

Then the boy looked down at the fair head between his knees. Suddenly he noticed that the man had grains of white sand in his hair, and the fair head was flecked with long green tendrils of seaweed.

The man was taking longer and longer strides, and the boy imagined that the sounds they made were louder and heavier and his feet were striking the ground harder. Then the boy had the feeling that he was looking at the shore and at the sea from a greater height. He looked down once more and instead of the fair head of hair, he saw a long neck with a thick grey mane and a large horse's head. The boy realized that he was sitting on that beautiful grey horse which had caught his heart so, when it had galloped away into the hills.

The horse galloped and pranced all round the shore, and ran into the shallow water until it splashed high into the air. Then he stopped, pawed the sand with his hoof and tossed his head. Joyfully the boy patted the horse's neck and cried out: 'Run, little horse, run.' And the horse reared up, took a few more high leaps, and set off at a gallop straight into the sea. The torn coils of mist spun and then closed behind them again and from somewhere far away in the mist a loud neigh rang out – or it could even have been the sound of triumphant human laughter.

On that spot where the horse ran into the sea, the imprint of horseshoes remained on the sandy shore. But the tracks led out of the sea . . .

Hanaaumoe

In ancient times, the island of Oahu was said to be the home of ghosts and evil spirits who fed on human flesh and devoured everyone who landed on their shores. The rumour spread swiftly and sailors began to steer clear of those waters. And so it happened that the spirits were often very hungry, for only rarely did they manage to ensnare some sailor who had lost his bearings or the survivor of a shipwreck, washed upon the shores of their island by a storm.

Therefore, the king of the ghosts and spirits appointed one of his subjects, the cruel and cunning spirit Hanaaumoe, to stand guard on the shore and persuade sailors to land on the island. Hanaaumoe could make himself appear pleasant and he talked persuasively, telling sailors that there were hardly any evil spirits left on the island, and those that remained had not been eating people for a long time, and so he often succeeded in tricking unsuspecting travellers.

One day, Kahaookamoku, who was a friend of the ruler of the island Kauai, came sailing into the waters around the island of Oahu. He commanded an impressive fleet of many rowers, and included among them was the lame Kaneope. They were bound for the island of Hawaii.

When Hanaaumoe caught sight of them, he began to call out to them from the shore:

'Do not go to Hawaii, why do you not know that evil spirits have overrun the island? No one escapes from them, they seize and devour every one. Land here, where you will have all you ask for, for here there is plenty of food and drink, and we have so many beautiful girls that each rower may have two, and your captain Kahaookamoku five, if he pleases.'

Kahaookamoku's crew was weary after their long voyage, and they were not opposed to the thought of resting for a

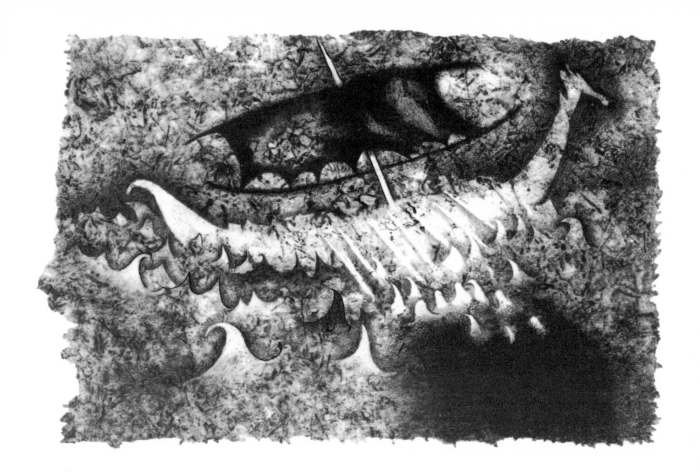

while, particularly when Hanaaumoe promised them so much. In the end, Kahaookamoku too was persuaded, and he gave orders for the ships to make port.

Hanaaumoe led them to a long house which stood a little distance from the shore, showed them where they were to sleep, and before long the sailors fell into a heavy sleep. Only the lame Kaneope did not sleep. In a little while, Hanaaumoe came into the house and asked:

'Well now, sailors, are you sleeping?'

The lame Kaneope replied:

'No, we are not sleeping, because we are waiting for the food and drink which you promised us.'

'You must be patient,' said Hanaaumoe, 'the way here is long, over mountains and forests, and we have not been able to transport the feast here yet.'

At midnight, Hanaaumoe came into the house again.

'Well now, sailors, are you sleeping?' he asked.

'No, we are not sleeping,' said Kaneope, 'because we are waiting for the young women. You said that you would give each rower two and our captain Kahaookamoku five.'

Again Hanaaumoe made excuses and went away. But Kaneope did not believe him, for he knew that the island of Oahu was full of ghosts and evil spirits who fed on human flesh. Therefore, he began to look for a hiding place. He decided to dig a hole for himself under the threshold, for if the ghosts came, their king would certainly sit at the threshold, and no one would dare to look for him under their king. And he set himself to the task at once. He scarcely had time to take cover, with no time to spare to warn captain Kahaookamoku of what danger threatened them. Without warning, Hanaaumoe came into the house and asked:

'Are you sleeping, sailors?'

And when no one answered him, he laughed and said:

'You fools, if you wished to sleep, you should have stayed at home, because here we shall eat you all.'

Upon which all the ghosts and spirits came hurtling into the room at once, led by their king Halalii, who sat on the threshold. There were so many of them that it would be impossible to count them. They pounced on the sailors, and in the twinkling of an eye they had eaten them all. Then they began to dig in the ground beneath the floor to make certain that no one had escaped them. They dug up the whole floor, avoiding only the threshold, where their king sat. And so Kaneope was saved.

When morning came, the ghosts and spirits all returned to their homes. Kaneope waited until no one was in sight and crept from his hiding-place. He escaped to the shore, climbed aboard one of the boats and swiftly sailed away. Hanaaumoe, who only saw him when he was some distance from the shore, thought that this was new prey arriving, and he began to lure him to the island, but Kaneope said:

'You are a ghost who devoured all our oarsmen, even captain Kahaookamoku.'

And he rowed relentlessly, to be as far away as soon as possible.

When he arrived on the island of Kauai, he told the king and all the people what had befallen him. The king decided at once that he would revenge himself on the ghosts, but he did not know how to go about it. He asked the wise man, Hanakapiai, who gave him this advice:

'Call all your master carpenters together and have them carve as many wooden statues as possible which are indistinguishable from living people.'

The king acted according to his counsel and instructed so many statues to be carved that a whole fleet was needed to transport them. Each one so faithfully resembled a human being, that it was difficult to distinguish them from the crew. And the whole fleet with all the statues and a multitude of warriors set sail for the island of Oahu.

The evil spirit Hanaaumoe saw them from afar, and he called out to them as he always did. Kaneope recognized him at once and warned all the others. But in front of the ghost they acted as though they suspected nothing. They landed where he showed them, disembarked and let themselves be led to the very same house where the ghosts had eaten captain Kahaookamoku and his crew. They spread the wooden statues which they brought with them out on the floor and then quietly returned to their boats.

After it had grown dark, Hanaaumoe went into the house and asked, as he did each time:

'Well now, sailors, are you sleeping?'

There was no sound. Hanaaumoe laughed and said:

'You fools, your end is near. Now we shall eat you all, as we ate those who slept here before you. If you wished to sleep, you should have stayed at home.'

And immediately all the ghosts and spirits led by their king Halalii surged into the house and began to gnaw on the wooden statues.

'But these are scrawny morsels,' they said in surprise. 'All of them are so stringy that it is impossible to take a good bite out of them. Not one of them is properly fattened. Why those which we ate last time were much better.'

They grumbled like this, but realized nothing.

In the meantime, the king gave instructions to his warriors for each of them to prepare a flaming torch, and then all at once, each of them flung his torch at the house. The walls, which were made of rushes and grass, burst into flame and all the ghosts and evil spirits perished in the blaze.

From that day forth, there was safety on the island of Oahu, and people no longer steered clear of it. They settled there and live there to this day.

Some say that the ghost Hanaaumoe managed to escape and he is supposedly in hiding somewhere. Indeed, he was certainly clever enough to do so – but because no one has heard even a whisper about him since that day, it is probably not true after all.

The Midnight Contest

It was the beginning of a long winter. The reindeer herds were already safe in their winter pasture in the sheltered valley beyond the forest, and the people, too, were preparing their huts for the time of frost and snow.

The snow was not deep as yet, but already hungry wolves were circling around the herds, waiting for their chance to strike. So the young men put on their skis and rode to the winter pastures to take turns at guarding the herds. When Hotti's turn came round, the weather was fine, and the reindeer pawed contentedly at the snow looking underneath for something good to eat. And so, close to midnight, Hotti hitched up the sledge and happily rode off home, a cloud of powdery snow rising behind him.

He was riding down the long slope alongside the forest; he slackened the reins and enjoyed the speed of the restless young reindeer that was pulling his sledge. When he was about halfway down the slope, the sound of a long sharp whistle rang out from the forest. Hotti was surprised and wondered what it could have been. No Laplander would whistle; a stranger would hardly be strolling through the forest at that hour, and it was definitely not an animal sound. When the whistling sounded again, Hotti brought the sledge to a halt and listened. But there was absolute silence in the forest; no footfall, nor the slightest rustle could be heard, and the whistle was not repeated.

Hotti became uneasy at the unexpected silence and he urged the reindeer forward and they sped on, hurrying to get home. Soon his hut came into view at the foot of the slope beneath the forest, and he could see smoke from the fireplace rising above the roof. Hotti urged the reindeer on once more, but as he came closer he saw a dark, motionless figure standing in front on his house. Then he saw that it was a man with a pointed red hat, a long knife hanging from his gleaming silver lamp. The man strode forward to meet Hotti and at the same time a large black dog who had been lying at his feet rose up and followed him.

The man stepped into Hotti's path, glared at him and rolled his eyes, which glittered in a face bordered by heavy black whiskers. Then he spoke out in a thunderous voice:

'I have come to challenge you to a fight. When the moon is full we shall meet on the cliff above the lake. Beware, we shall fight to the death.'

Before Hotti could recover from his surprise, his challenger turned on his heel and strode away into the forest with his black dog. He had only taken a few paces, when both of them suddenly melted into thin air and vanished. Neither the man nor the dog left any footprints in the snow.

The next day Hotti was silent; he confided in no one about his experience of the night before, and he thought of nothing but his strange nocturnal visitor. When he realized that he could not solve the mystery alone, he set off towards the lake, where old Skuorra was spending the winter. Everyone said that he was the wisest man in the world and many people were grateful to him for his wise counsel.

Hotti told Skuorra of his experience and asked him what he should do. Skuorra thought and then he said:

'Hard times await you, young man. That black man with the black dog was a revengeful spirit. Someone wants to harm you and has sent a stallu to get you. They like to fight and the smallest excuse is enough for them. Think hard. Have you any enemies, or have you had an argument with anyone? If you were to make your peace, the stallu would no longer have any power over you.'

Hotti considered for a long time and finally he replied:

'I do not know that I have any enemies among the people of this land. But I remember something that happened to me in the summer. While we were branding the reindeer in the summer pastures, I argued with an unknown man about a stray calf. He had an evil face, and when I would not give him the calf, because it was ours, he kept looking at me for a long time as though he were saying something to himself. But I cannot make peace with him, because I do not know him and I do not know where he came from.'

'That is bad,' sighed Skuorra. 'In that case you will have to go and fight the stallu. For if you do not meet his challenge, you will fall into his power. He will destroy your herds, your

95

family, and in the end, you, too. But if you fight against him, you stand a good chance of defeating him, for you are young and strong.'

Then Skuorra reflected and after a moment he continued:

'But it will not be enough for you to overcome him and knock him down. You must kill him. Otherwise he will challenge you again and he will fight with you until he defeats you, and then it will cost you your life, as he himself has told you. If you succeed in overcoming him, he will beg you for mercy, but you must not listen to him. Stab him with your knife under his arm. That is the only place where he is vulnerable, because he is clad in iron. So be prepared for a merciless battle.'

Hotti thanked him for his counsel and was already leaving, when Skuorra called him back and said to him:

'Remember one more thing. If you succeed in killing the stallu, you must also kill his dog. Otherwise you will never have peace.'

When the full moon rose and the appointed night came, Hotti returned from his vigil with the herds, and skied out of the forest and turned towards the lake.

A great deal of snow had fallen and the black patch of the lake had shrunk as the water froze near the shores. Hotti stepped out on the cliff above the lake, laid aside his skis, leaned against the trunk of an uprooted tree and looked about. The snow glistened in the light of the moon; there was not a breath of wind and all was utterly silent. Suddenly a wild whistling pierced the air, and in a flash the black figure of the stallu appeared on the cliff.

The stallu rolled his flashing eyes and said in his harsh voice:

'I am glad that you are brave and have come to wrestle with me. Defend yourself!'

He spread out his arms and with straddling steps, he slowly closed in on Hotti. Hotti crouched down a little and when the stallu came within arm's reach, he suddenly lashed out violently and thrust at him with such force that the stallu stumbled. But he did not succeed in knocking him down, and so they locked together in close combat. The cold breath of the stallu blew over Hotti; the nearness of his evil eyes filled him with horror, and the stallu held him in a crushing embrace. Hotti braced himself firmly and was careful not to lose his balance. They wrestled for a long time in this way, turning in circles, until at last Hotti succeeded in seizing his enemy by his silver belt. He gathered up all his strength, lifted

the stallu and knocked his feet out from under him. The stallu fell on his back so heavily that the ground trembled. He pressed him against the ground, and was catching his breath when the stallu spoke out:

'You are truly strong and fearless. You have won. Let me go and I shall serve you.'

But Hotti did not reply and drew his knife from his belt. The stallu began to plead:

'Do not kill me, I only challenged you to a contest. Let me go, I beg you. I will give you my silver belt.'

But remembering the words of Skuorra, Hotti ignored his pleas, and with all his might stabbed him under the left arm. When he saw that the stallu was no longer moving, he stood up, exhausted from the battle, and rested against a tree trunk and gazed at his fallen foe. He did not even notice when his knife slipped from his hand and fell into the snow.

Suddenly something black appeared beside the fallen stallu and Hotti remembered that he had still to slay the dog. But before he had gathered the strength to do so, it was too late. The black dog bowed over his master and began to lick his wound. Before long the stallu came to life. He stood up and said:

'You have won this battle. But I am challenging you to fight me again here, at the next full moon. And remember that I, too, will show no mercy,' he added. Then both he and his dog vanished.

The exhausted Hotti hardly knew how he got home. When he awoke in the morning, he set off once again to the hut by the lake and told Skuorra how though he had won the battle, he had not defeated his persecutor.

'He is evidently a strong stallu, and you would probably not be strong enough to vanquish him alone. The next time, I shall go with you and if you succeed in overcoming him, I shall take care of his dog. I shall use a gun against him, but because I shall only be your helper, I must load it with a silver bullet. An ordinary bullet would not kill him, and I do not know whether you would be capable of fighting a third time.'

Four weeks went by, and more snow fell, until it covered the cliff above the lake. The lake, too, was frozen over, except for a tiny black speck far from the shore. Hotti and his helper climbed up to the snow-covered cliff by the light of the moon. Skuorra hid himself behind the roots of a fallen tree and Hotti waited for his opponent.

Before long they heard the whistle; the stallu appeared and immediately hurled himself at Hotti. This time, the battle

lasted longer, and Hotti was almost swooning, when at last he succeeded in knocking the stallu to the ground. With his last remaining strength he stabbed him, then his vision blackened, and he heard a shot ring out as if from a great distance.

When Hotti regained consciousness, he saw that he was lying beside the dead stallu and the shot black dog. Skuorra helped him to his feet and said:

'We have overcome him, but you are not safe yet. There are many stallus, and if they found his body here, they would hunt you down to avenge him.'

And so they dragged the dead stallu and his black dog all the way to the middle of the lake. They tied the dog to the body and watched, as the stallu, with his heavy iron armour, sank to the bottom of the lake.

Only then could Hotti, tired to death, go home. Only then could he ride peacefully again to the herds in the winter pasture and look forward to the spring and to the long journey to the summer pastures in the north.

The Flying
Heads

A young man with a walking stick in his hand and a shabby satchel over his shoulder walked along a path winding through the undergrowth alongside a mountain stream. On his head he had a wide hat woven of bamboo, and on his feet a pair of tattered sandals. He had been travelling for some time, and he was in no particular hurry. For he had the unpleasant duty of explaining why, for the second time, he had failed to pass the official examinations in the capital city, even though he had studied for them for three years. For this reason he did not choose the shortest route home, nor did he select the most comfortable means of travelling. Instead he rambled on foot through out-of-the-way places. Places which he had only heard people talk of before.

The path alongside the stream ran into the mountains and twisted so intricately that the luckless student Hoa Phieu no longer had the vaguest notion of where he actually was. However, he was confident that eventually he would be able to ask for directions and he was satisfied that, despite all the detours, he was always travelling south in the direction of home.

He went a good distance further, when suddenly the path swerved away from the stream and veered directly into the scrub. The only sounds were the twittering of birds and insects buzzing in the hot sun. Hoa wearily scrambled up the steep path, resting now and then, and wondered whether he would find some sort of human habitation in this deserted place, where he could spend the night. But he comforted himself with the thought that the path would surely lead somewhere where he could spend the night, and he continued his journey in confidence.

As he approached the crest of the hill, the undergrowth

thinned a little and he could see a massive stone structure above him. On closer inspection, it turned out to be a crumbling fortress built on the rocky plateau above a sheer precipice which dropped into the next valley. The white stones gleamed in the evening sun, and creepers swayed gently in the evening breeze.

Hoa stepped into the courtyard, and as he walked round the stone well in the centre, he saw that one building among the ruins still had a roof on it. It had sturdy walls and a tiled roof, and it looked like some sort of storehouse. It also appeared that the old storehouse was not as deserted as the rest of the castle, as if someone might still be living there. Hoa rejoiced that he had found a place where he could ask for a night's lodgings.

He stepped up to the door and peered cautiously inside. When his eyes grew accustomed to the gloom, he saw a still figure sitting in the corner on the other side of the room. Hoa took off his hat, set down his bag, leaned his staff against the wall, and with a bow, stepped inside. An old man with a clean-shaven head and a long, sparse grey beard sat on a mat in the corner. He was dressed in a shabby, rust-coloured sarong which may once have been yellow. The old man replied to Hoa's greeting with nothing more than a nod of his head and without a word, pointed to a second mat lying against the wall next to the door. Hoa sat down and when the old man did not speak, he remained silent and rested. Presently it began to grow dark, and Hoa, feeling refreshed, stood up and stretched.

'Where do you want to go?' the old man suddenly asked.

'I want to go and wash in that well,' replied Hoa startled.

'Do not do that,' said the old man in a warning voice. 'Here you may wash only in flowing water, and you cannot reach it now before dark.' After a while he added: 'But bring your staff inside.'

Astonished Hoa obeyed, and before he could think about what the old man's words could mean, the sun went down, dark night fell and a mild wind began to blow.

The old man lit a torch and offered his guest a little cold rice and a cup of weak tea. Then he settled himself down to sleep and turned his face to the wall. But after a while he turned his head and said:

'If anything should happen in the night, no matter what it is, do not be afraid, pay no attention and no harm will come to you. I expect nothing will happen, but just to make sure, I want to tell you that under no circumstances are you to go outside. And what is more, you had better not even go near the window or the door.' When he finished speaking, he turned towards the wall once more and apparently fell asleep at once.

Hoa sat up a little while longer, looking through the large empty window into the darkness and wondering what mysterious events were to take place there, but then his eyes began to close and he too fell asleep.

He was woken by an appalling scream which echoed from the valley below the precipice. There was horror in it, and also fury, and it was so piercing that Hoa caught his breath in shock. Then he saw by the light of the moon that something was flying through the air. Suddenly he realized that they were human heads. Their long black hair fluttered in the wind, and the screaming was coming from their gaping mouths. They flew by, one after the other, and in the distance he could see a huge throng of heads hovering over the valley.

One head flew close by the window; it stopped in mid-air and stared inside. It was very pale, almost white; its huge rigid eyes were bulging and reddened, sharp teeth showed in its gaping mouth, and long black strands of hair billowed in the wind. For a moment it stared intently at the terror-struck Hoa, then it shook itself angrily and flew away.

Meanwhile the old man had woken. He waited until Hoa had recovered a little from his shock, poured him another cup of tea, and then said:

'I am not fond of unnecessary words, and because I hoped that they would not come today, I said nothing about them to you. But now that you have seen them, I shall tell you something about them.'

The old man fell silent, gazed for a long time into the night, and then continued:

'In ancient times, a foreign race inhabited these mountains. They were wise people, they lived in peace, they worked and prospered. But they were proud and valiant, they wished to live on their own and refused to submit to the king's rule. For many years they fought courageously against the king's soldiers, but their land grew smaller and smaller. They no longer had time for their fields, and they were not happy with a life of continual warfare, so in the end the remaining warriors laid down their arms and surrendered. But the king was enraged by the long war, in which he had lost so many of his best warriors, and he was afraid that in time he would have to take up arms again against this arrogant race. And so he had the whole race destroyed, warriors, old men, women and children. Only a very few of them escaped death.'

The old man gazed into the emptiness again, sighed, and then took up his story:

'The flying heads which you saw belong to the ghosts of those he executed. In the daytime these ghosts look like ordinary living people, but in the night, when they lie down to sleep some of their heads split free from their bodies, hover above the valley and avenge themselves on all living people for the ancient wrong. They cannot enter a human dwelling, though, and only kill those who remain outside under the open sky at night. But they also have power over anyone who leaves something that belongs to him outside, or something that was in contact with his body. When they find something like that outside a house, they take possession of it and through it, they destroy the life of the person who was not as careful as he should have been.'

The old man finished speaking and remained seated, and Hoa also fell deep into thought over the cruel and terrible tale. Suddenly, an appalling shriek rang out, and another head appeared at the window, with hair tossing wildly in the wind.

Hoa dropped his bowl in fright and the tea spilled out over the stone floor. The head noticed it, twitched, flew quickly to the door and eagerly watched as the thin stream of liquid ran slowly towards the threshold. Hoa also noticed it, but he was so dazed that he was unable to move and he could not tear his eyes away from the slow trickle of tea.

Then suddenly and unexpectedly swiftly, the old man leapt up and with a corner of his sarong stopped and dried the spilled tea just in time, before it could run onto the threshold.

With that the head waiting at the door vanished, and for the rest of the night all was peaceful.

In the morning the old man woke the restlessly sleeping Hoa and said to him:

'I shall go with you down into the valley to show you the way out of this region. I do not know whether you will be able to find shelter for another night, and you have already seen what danger threatens you.'

A winding path along the mountainside led them down into the valley, and no sooner had they stepped out from the undergrowth, than a village appeared before them. Hoa rejoiced, but then he saw that there was something odd about the village. The houses had no walls and the roofs were caved in, but even stranger, though, were its inhabitants. They were sturdy and had long black hair, but they merely loitered about; they stood or sat by their houses. They did nothing;

they did not speak, nor did they notice the newcomers, but only stared blankly into space.

'These are the people,' said the old man. 'You can recognize them by their reddened eyes. There are several villages of them, neither dead nor alive, and only here and there scattered among them lives some poor soul or a hermit such as myself.'

Hoa was saddened by what he saw and he sighed:

'Could someone not free them from this curse?'

The old man slowly shook his head and then said:

'Perhaps only time, time transforms everything, and ultimately even injuries are buried by the sands of time.'

Then he led the young man far beyond the village to a river, showed him the ford and bade him farewell:

'There on the other bank you will be in safety. Go home and live happily.'

The Strange
Illness

Under the wide arching heavens extends a boundless fertile plain. Villages are hidden among the tall stalks of wheat, villages whose serene life has for hundreds of years been fixed by the changeless cycle of ploughing, sowing and reaping. And yet the eternal peace of this region was one day disturbed. One remote village suddenly fell prey to an unknown illness. Not a week went by without a procession dressed in black emerging from the little church on the hill. Behind the biers, on which lay plainer and plainer coffins, hastily constructed, walked fewer and fewer survivors. After a few months, only the old parson and a villager who had taken on the task of gravedigger were left. The rest of the living closed their shutters and locked their doors, but nothing helped against the unidentified disease.

It was probably some unknown plague; for even learned doctors put their heads together in vain to investigate what this strange, inexplicable illness could be. The afflicted did not suffer from fever, nor did they complain of any pain; for a few days they were the victims of nightmares so oppressive that they could scarcely catch their breath, and after a few days they died. Everyone in the region avoided the stricken village, over which lay a dark blanket of untold horror.

To all this misfortune yet another circumstance was added, which heightened the villagers' dread of the unkown evil.

As soon as it grew dark, huge bats whirled in silent flight above the low roofs of the houses and in the deserted courtyards, and it seemed to everyone that there were more and more of them each day. This is more like a village of bats, the villagers began to whisper fearfully.

Rumours of the strange illness and the dying village for which there was no help spread all the way to the capital.

There it reached the ears of the old librarian Balazs. He
listened with interest to the accounts of the illness and its
symptoms, and to the vast astonishment of his friends, he
packed his bags one day and rode out of the city.

He went straight to that distressed village. As he walked
through the village, he met no one, and so he made his way to
the parsonage to see the old parson, whom he knew was still
alive.

'I know that it seems extraordinary to you that such an old
man, and a bookworm such as I, has come to offer you his
services. I have read a considerable number of books in my
lifetime, and when I heard people describe this strange
pestilence which has appeared in one village, it seemed
familiar to me. I have certainly read about such cases, I
thought, and as it turned out, I was not mistaken. If what is
happening here in your village is indeed what is written up in
books, then the remedy will be simple.'

The parson rejoiced. He was grateful to see someone who
was not afraid to come into the village. Since springtime,
everyone had been avoiding them. He gladly described the

symptoms, and then told Balazs how the village was tormented by bats. Why they had already made their way into the church, and were gnawing the candles on the altar! Balazs listened to the parson and then asked this question:

'How did it actually begin? Who was the very first to die?'

The parson reflected: 'Wait a moment now, who was actually the first? It began in the springtime of last year, and so I get it all muddled. You see, it is actually difficult to decide who was the first one – whether it was Juliska from the lower estate or her fiancé Lajos.'

The parson thought back: Juliska was a beautiful young girl who loved to laugh and work became child's play in her hands. He would often joke with her and tell her that whoever took her as his wife would fare very well, but that she ought to choose one of the local young men, for he would be sad if she went somewhere far away. Juliska would toss her head and say that she was in no hurry to be married and that she was happy at home. But last year during the carnival she became engaged to the neighbour's boy, the handsome Lajos. The wedding, however, never took place, for Lajos had to go away into the army. Juliska promised him that she would not marry and that she would wait for him even if it meant until her death. And she waited for him faithfully. She stayed at home, she did not even go dancing. That was it, she was the very first who was struck down by this tragedy – the parson interrupted his recollections – but I really must tell it to you properly, one thing at a time.

Last spring a rumour spread through the village that Lajos had deserted from the army. He was lonely for Juliska, and so he simply packed up and went home. But on his way, he mysteriously met his death somewhere. It must have been

close to our village, because people saw him in this region. But his body was never found, only a little bundle full of his things lay somewhere out in the fields.

A few days after this news, Juliska came to the parsonage. She had not come for confession, oh no, she had only come to seek the old parson's advice, for she no longer knew where to turn. The parson calmed and comforted her. He thought that the poor girl was grieving for Lajos, and so he told her that after all it had not been confirmed at all that Lajos was dead. But Juliska grew more and more agitated, until finally she blurted out:

'I have talked with Lajos,' and feverishly she let forth a torrent of words, as though she were afraid she would not finish everything she wanted to say.

It had not been long ago, she said. It had happened only a few days before. Everyone in the house was asleep and she too was preparing for bed. All was quiet, only the moon shone brightly, for the moon was full. She was thinking of Lajos and wishing so very much that he were with her. All of a sudden, someone tapped softly at the window. Juliska started in fright, but when the tapping sounded again, she cautiously drew aside the curtain. On the other side of the window stood Lajos! And in the light of the moon, he had such a pallid face. Quickly she opened the window and let him in. She questioned him about all sorts of things, but Lajos did not answer her and only smiled at her enigmatically. Just before daybreak he went away. And the next day she learned that Lajos was no longer among the living. She was horrified, and she was ashamed to say that he could not possibly be dead, when he had been with her that night.

Juliska waited anxiously for evening to come. Perhaps Lajos would come once again and would explain everything to her. And Lajos indeed came. Again he tapped softly at the window and his face was just as pale. He would not answer her questions, and this time his smile was ominous. Juliska grew frightened of him. She asked him to leave, but Lajos would not go, not until just before dawn. From that time on, he came every night. And she was so terrified by then that she locked herself in, she would not answer the tapping, but even when she closed the window tightly, Lajos appeared in her room. And she was feeling worse and worse. She had no one to confide in, for she could not possibly tell her parents about it.

The parson felt sorry for her. What sat before him was not the happy Juliska of last year, but her pale, tormented shadow. He tried to talk to her, telling her that she was imagining it all out of terrible grief at the loss of Lajos.

'Oh yes, I comforted her, poor thing,' sighed the parson, 'until she did feel a little better and finally returned home. In the morning she was found dead. It was indeed a sad funeral,' he recalled. 'The bride had died and we knew nothing about the groom.'

'And you see,' the parson turned to his guest, 'that was when the strange illness began. Juliska's mother complained that she was tormented by nightmares, for a few days she went about with reddened eyes and then she quietly passed away. Soon afterwards she was followed by the father, and next the younger sister. Then I gave funerals to the members of Lajos's family and now I cannot even list them for you, the way one funeral followed the other. Why, there are only a few of us left living in the village. I devoted entire days to prayer, I wrote for help everywhere possible, but it was all no use. They even went so far as to be astonished that I remain here. But surely I am not going to desert my lambs in times of misfortune!'

The old librarian listened attentively to the parson's story. A flicker of understanding now and again flashed in his eyes, and seemingly inappropriately, he would blurt out, yes, that is it, yes yes, that is how it is. The parson was so absorbed in his own recollections that he did not even notice his remarks. When he had finished, he sighed and said:

'And that is everything. I wonder who will arrange my funeral, when my turn comes. May God grant that I might at least be the last to die!'

The librarian wrung his hands with impatience.

'Far from it, my dear parson, the end to all this horror is at hand. This is quite a clear case. I have read about it several times. It is not some plague that devastates this village, but vampires!'

'Vampires? You, such a learned man, believe in vampires?' asked the parson in astonishment.

'Believe or disbelieve, just consider carefully what has been happening here.' The librarian was impatient. A pity that it was night, otherwise he would have set to work at once. First of all, he advised the parson to tell all those who remained alive in the village to hang garlic about everywhere.

'Everyone must have it on his person at all times, and must hang it in all windows and doors,' he commanded.

The parson found it ridiculous, but when a parson does not know where else to turn, he catches at every straw. The villagers thought the same, and without protest they took the librarian's advice.

Insistently he urged the parson: 'We have before us a difficult task. In order to bring the raging of the vampires to an end once and for all, we must open the graves of all those who died this year. Write to the count, we must obtain a permit to open the graves.'

So for several days the parson wrote letters in which he again described in detail everything that had happened in the village, including librarian Balazs's explanation and his request.

Some time later, the permit to open the fresh graves arrived. Balazs ordered stakes to be hewn from the wood of the linden tree, as many stakes as there were bodies. Then he, together with the parson and a number of villagers, made their way to the cemetery.

How great was the astonishment of them all when they opened the grave and coffin of Juliska, who died in the beginning of spring. The dead girl lay in her coffin unimpaired, her cheeks were rosy, her skin was taut, just as though she were alive. And the same was in all the rest of the graves.

Balazs explained to the horrified villagers that they next had to drive the stakes of linden wood into the chests of the bodies. Only then would they free their souls of their curse and save themselves as well. After lengthy persuasion, they finally steeled themselves to do it. The instant they drove the wooden stake into the chest of the corpse they heard a deep sigh, and fresh blood spurted from the mouth and nose of the dead one. And in the same instant, the body was transformed into a true corpse, the cheeks sank and a blissful smile settled on the lips. When they had done the same to all the corpses, the parson arranged new funerals for them all.

Then began a painstaking search for the body of Lajos. Lajos had no doubt been killed on his way by a vampire, and he who dies at the hands of a vampire becomes a vampire himself, and he returns to his own people, lured by either homesickness or memories. And he harms them even against his own will, until he is set free by an honest death. And so the villagers searched the fields, out-of-the-way paths and trails, until finally they came upon young Lajos. He looked as though he were sleeping, curled up in some thick bushes. They could not believe he was dead, and they lost the courage to drive the linden stake into his chest, as they had done to the corpses in the cemetery. But finally they quelled their dread and plunged the stake forcefully into Lajos's chest. At the very same instant, blood spurted forth from his nose and mouth, and on his fast-disintegrating face there appeared a blissful smile.

The villagers gave Lajos a proper funeral, and peace and quiet were restored to the village. The old librarian Balazs packed up his bags, and happily returned to his books. To the teasing of his friends, he would now reply:

'Just never mind. These old dead books can still be of service to the living.'

The Snow
Woman

Two children, nine-year-old Eiko and a little boy named Haruo lived with their family in a farmhouse on the southern tip of the village. One day, after many days of snow, the weather cleared; the sky was a brilliant blue, and the snow sparkled in the sun. Though the air was frosty, everyone was thankful that at last they could go outside again. Ever since morning, Eiko had been begging her mother to allow her and her brother to visit their aunt. The weather was fine, and so their mother consented and both children ran joyfully out of the house.

The sun was high in the sky when suddenly it began to grow dark, and the sky was swiftly overcast with heavy snow clouds.

'Another dreadful blizzard is coming! I had better go and fetch the children, or they will not be able to return home today,' said their mother as she threw her quilted jacket over her shoulders and ran out on the snow-covered path. She hurried to her sister's house at the other end of the village, but her children were not there.

'I sent them off more than an hour ago,' said the children's aunt. 'Eiko remembered that her uncle from the city was to come to visit you today, and she was restless. So she took the little one on her back and went.'

'We probably missed one another on the way. I will run home quickly, it will start snowing any minute.'

But the children were not at home.

What if they went to meet their uncle, the mother thought in fright. They are bound to lose their way in this blizzard and darkness. I must find them! And at once she ran out and down the path which led through the woods to the nearby city. She hardly passed the last house in the village, when it grew even

darker, and a sharp blast of icy wind blew in from the sea. It swirled up the snow on the path and seemed to tear the heavy, low-hanging clouds. A deluge of snow spilled down from the sky, so that soon not even the path was visible.

The mother tried to think where her children could possibly be, where they might have taken shelter from the blizzard, and if they could have fallen into a snowdrift somewhere. Then tales she had heard about the snow monster Yukionna flashed through her mind, and in horror she imagined the terrible white monster clutching her children in its icy embrace. Desparately she cried, 'Eiko! Haruo!', but the swirling snow and the howling of the wind drowned her voice so that she could scarcely hear her own calling.

With an effort she waded on through the snow, where she sensed the path was. The blizzard thickened, but after a little while the wind died down as abruptly as it had begun. It even grew a little brighter and only the large flakes of snow fell quietly. Then the mother discovered that she had strayed from the path into the fields during the blizzard. Then she noticed a figure a short distance in front of her who was carrying something. Perhaps it is Eiko with Haruo, she thought, and hastily she floundered through the snow towards them.

Soon she realized that it was not Eiko, but a woman coming from the city. She carried something wrapped in a woollen shawl in her arms. The mother ran towards her and asked her:

'Please, have you passed two children somewhere on your way, a young girl and a little boy? They lost their way during the blizzard and I cannot find them.'

The woman drew her shawl covered with snowflakes back from her forehead with a gentle hand. A beautiful, smooth face with shining eyes appeared, and on it a kindly smile.

'No I am afraid not, dear lady, but there under the tree I found this little boy. He is still a baby. The poor thing was stiff with cold and was crying. So I wrapped him in my shawl and took him with me. Could he possibly be yours?'

Oh, could it possibly be Haruo, the mother thought in fright and she reached her arms out towards the infant. She did not even notice the woman handing him to her, and already she held him in her arms. All of a sudden she felt him grow heavy in her arms, and icy cold. She wanted to turn aside the shawl and look at the child, but she no longer had the strength to move her arms. Her arms began to chill and turn to ice. The child in her arms grew heavier and heavier, it pulled her towards the ground. The woman was silent and looked at

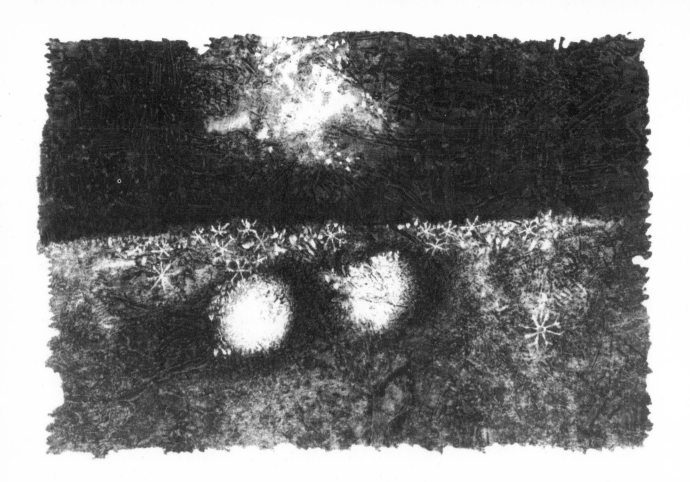

the mother with the same kindly expression and a smile that seemed frozen on her pale lips.

All at once a violent gust of icy wind rose up, and it swirled around the woman and engulfed her in a stream of snow. Suddenly nothing remained of her but a high swirling column of snowflakes, and within them, a barely perceptible face with a rigid smile and evilly glittering eyes.

The mother was just about to sink under the dreadful burden in her arms, and the terrible cold was closing round her heart. The wind curled aside a corner of the shawl – and she saw a tiny baby, utterly white, covered with snowflakes, unmoving, all of ice. In a swoon, the mother saw blackness before her eyes, she sank to her knees, and at the same time she heard an anguished calling, coming as if from a great distance: 'Mummy! Mummy!' They were the voices of Eiko and Haruo.

She pulled herself together and with her last ounce of strength, she loosened her arms and dropped the deadly piece of ice. Instantly the apparition vanished. The mother knelt on the freshly snow-covered path and a wide expanse of powdery snow stretched around her, marked here and there by strange tracks.

Her children and their uncle were running up the path towards her.

'Mummy, has anything happened to you?'

'We saw from a distance that you were talking to someone here,' said their uncle. 'But when you fell down and that eddy of snow appeared around you, I knew at once that it was Yukionna bent on destroying you. Thank goodness that we were just coming. And also that the children met me before that blizzard. Yukionna was no doubt lying in wait for them.'

'That was Yukionna, the snow woman?' the mother asked in astonishment. 'I thought that Yukionna was some sort of white monster, and not such a beautiful lady.'

'Yes, that was Yukionna, the beautiful white lady who heralds death,' their uncle confirmed. 'Do you see those strange tracks in the snow? She does not have legs, and hovers above the ground. Only sometimes when she comes to rest, her kimono brushes the snow and indents it a little.'

The children stared in fright at the depressions in the snow, but their uncle bade them hurry, so that they might reach home before the snow began to fall again.

Captain Hasan, or the Lame One

His Majesty the sultan of Malaya rode out with all his court to his summer palace, Tanjong Bemban, to refresh himself from the dust of the city and to look once again at how his subjects in the country lived. During his stay, he heard stories about a certain Captain Hasan, whom they had nick-named Si Pinchang, or Lame One. Because there was nothing to do in the evenings to keep boredom at bay in the provinces, His Majesty charged the chief constable of the village to bring Captain Hasan into his presence.

When the old sailor appeared, His Majesty accepted his bow patronizingly and stated:

'We are pleased that you accepted Our invitation, Captain Hasan. We are a little bored and would like to hear some good stories. You are an old and experienced man – surely you can tell many remarkable tales?'

'I can indeed,' the old man confirmed. 'Your Magnificence's servant has sailed the whole circumference of this earth, and has experienced so many adventures on the high seas and in far-off lands, that he need not dream anything when he wishes to astound his listeners.'

'If that is so,' stated His Majesty, 'then tell us how you came to be called Si Pinchang.'

Captain Hasan settled down in his seat, cleared his throat and began.

'Many years ago, when Your Majesty's servant was still in his prime and had not a single wrinkle around his eyes, he sailed his ship out into the China Sea looking for trade. A favourable wind was blowing, and we sped along at a fine pace. In our hearts we were already counting the profit from our trade, when suddenly the sky clouded over and a fierce wind from our starboard side snatched us and carried us far from all known shores and islands. After ten days' running before the wind through an uncharted sea, we finally sighted land. We did not know the name of it, and to this day no one knows it. We dropped anchor in a bay, close to the mouth of a river. I do not even know the name of the river, and when I speak of it, I will refer to it simply as the River. When our boat landed on the shore, we were surrounded by small people with dark skin and straight, smooth hair. We had a difficult time understanding one another, for few of them knew one or two words of our language. They showed little interest in our goods, though they certainly knew what trade was, for we saw many things there that they did not make themselves, and saw store-houses full of merchandise – much more than they could possibly consume. It was obvious that they traded with someone. After some days, when I could make myself better understood, I began to inquire into their trade. They pointed up the River, and it occurred to me that there were possibly other more civilized people there to whom I could sell my goods at great profit. A longing for wealth and fame came over me, adventure lured me, and curiosity hounded me; and I began to plan an expedition up the River. I picked eight seamen – just the number of oarsmen that were needed for my boat – took food and samples of various goods on board, and in the morning, shortly after dawn, we pushed off and our journey began. The current of the River was not strong and we made good headway. Towards evening we arrived at a village which was not much more imposing than the one we had left in the morning. Indeed, there were even fewer inhabitants, and they showed little interest in our goods. And so the following morning we launched our boat once more and sailed on up the river. The next village was again one day's sailing distant. We were received better than before. The inhabitants appeared to be wealthier, but they were covered with old wounds and scars.

Ah, I said to myself, these are the visible signs of pirate raids which these natives wage against their much wealthier neighbours living further up the River. And this confirmed my decision to continue sailing. As we were boarding the boat in the morning, our hosts caught us by our arms and tried to prevent us from going. They even offered us gifts in order to dissuade us from further travel, but I saw in this nothing but a confirmation of my suspicions, and I said to myself:

These people do not want us to learn about the source of their wealth. They are afraid we will agree to trade and will deprive them of their spoils which they gain either as pirates

or in their dealings with the poorer natives downstream.

All of us were greedy for wealth, my seamen no less than myself. And although they rowed as best they could, the journey seemed to take much longer. This was mainly due to the treetrunks which blocked the river and forced us to go warily and make many detours. Then finally, shortly before nightfall, we caught sight of a village at a bend in the river, quite similar to those we had seen the previous days. These natives lived in long houses supported by posts, the floors were made of nothing more than a sort of lattice-work roughly covered with matting. Even the walls of these houses were made of matting, as well as the partitions between the rooms. One could hear every child that cried, every hen that scratched between the houses, and every pig that rooted about in the heaps of rubbish under the houses. It was cool though, and a refreshing breeze from the river blew through the rooms so I welcomed the thought of spending the night there.

When we landed, the natives came running and gathered around us, calling out and inspecting our merchandise with curiosity. I was delighted by their interest, and when I saw the elders of the village coming, I selected some costly gifts for them, hoping to arouse a lively interest in trade. But I was astonished when they in turn overwhelmed me with gifts costlier by far.

I understood from their gestures rather than their words that they heartily welcomed all of us to their village, and that they were preparing a banquet to welcome us. So I ordered my seamen to pull the boat up on the shore, and I allowed myself to be led by the villagers to the most imposing of the houses. I looked around for my men, and discovered that the villagers had divided them amongst themselves, and that they were leading each man into a different house. It did not seem proper to me that we were being separated like this, but I could do nothing to prevent it, not wishing to disrupt the hospitality that I believed existed in the villagers. All that I could do was to place my trust in their good intentions. I contented myself with the fact that the houses were not far from one another, and so everything that happened in one could be heard in all the rest. My seamen were better armed than these natives, and every one of them was experienced in fighting pirates – I relied on these circumstances and surrendered myself, along with my sailors, to the will of Allah.

As I said, they led me to the most impressive of the houses, and ushered me up steps hewn into the trunk of a mighty tree.

Once inside, they sat me down on an exquisite carpet, and delivering speeches in their language, began to lavish food and drink on me. I ate of everything that they offered and left nothing untasted.

The beverage which we drank did not seem particularly strong and I relied on my head and drank without fear. As it turned out I underestimated both the strength of that wine and my own tiredness. For in a little while, my eyelids began to grow heavy, and I was overcome by a strong urge to roll over on those mats and rugs and get a good sleep.

Everywhere in the world, it is the custom that a guest is inviolable in the house of his host. The behaviour of these people suggested that the same custom held true for them – I noticed nothing ominous in their behaviour, why I did not even notice any weapons in their house, and, therefore, I decided to give in to my fatigue. I lay down on the bed that had been prepared and before long, lulled by their quiet talk and the sweet sounds of their singing, I fell asleep.

I do not know how long I slept. I do not even know what awoke me but it was still dark when I opened my eyes.

The first thing I noticed was the unusual silence around me. I could hear nothing but my own breathing. The bright light of the moon filtered through the thin matted walls, and my eyes soon grew accustomed to the half-shadow. There was no one with me in the room, and not the slightest rustling indicated the presence of anyone in the house. Why had they all disappeared? I fell asleep surrounded by people – and now there was no one. I was alone in the house, surrounded by the strange silence. After a while, I realized that a strange noise could be heard, coming from beneath the floor of the house. I slipped from the bed and crawled to a spot where the matting failed to reach the wall. From there I could look through the lattice-work of the floor to see what was causing that strange noise.

I beheld a hideous herd of crocodiles, slithering about and crawling one on top of the other. The village has been invaded by crocodiles, I thought, and my hosts have fled from the house, either to take cover deeper in the forests, or to battle against these ghastly monsters. I reached for my weapons, but they were not where I had left them nor were they anywhere in the house. I felt myself whiten in fear, but then I comforted myself with the thought that their warriors had taken my weapons, which they realized were more effective than their own, and not wishing to wake me, as an honoured guest, were now using them in their defence and mine.

121

Then another thought struck me; why could I hear no sounds of battle? How was it that all these crocodiles were calmly crawling under this house? Could it be that the battle had already been fought? Was it possible that all the villagers had been devoured without the sound of a single cry, a single groan? Even if the villagers had died in silence, perhaps petrified with horror before those monsters, was it at all possible that not one of my crew had cried out to try to raise the alarm, or at least to warn the others? All this flashed through my mind, and I began to shout, to give the alarm, so that I at least might warn the others. It was also possible that the others might come to my help if they were hidden in the woods.

I drew attention to myself, and unfortunately, it was not altogether to my advantage. The hideous beasts raised their heads and began to slither towards the steps which led into the house. There was a vast number of them, and more came crawling from all sides. The most agile of them were climbing up the steps, were already poking their jaws full of needle-sharp teeth into the door of the house, and were already creeping towards me along the floor. I turned and fled from them, looking frantically around me for some weapon, or at least a stick which I could jam into their throats, when they got close enough to snap at me with their gaping jaws. By

a stroke of fortune, I succeeded in tearing a strong bamboo pole from the roof of the house, and managed to ram it down the throat of a young crocodile just as he was about to close his powerful jaws around my leg. Blood spurted from his throat but in spite of his wound, he was not prepared to give up. He started trying to pull the pole away from me. Before I could tear it away from him, the next huge crocodile was upon me, and he snapped at my calf with his terrible jaws. I felt a piercing pain and black spots formed before my eyes. But in that instant I succeeded in twisting my weapon free, and not even fully aware of what I was doing, I dealt a terrible blow to the crocodile who was gripping me by the leg. Perhaps I caused him such intense pain, or perhaps his jaws were already so decrepit with age that they let go – I do not know, I only felt that I had wrenched my leg from his grip and that for the moment I was free. With all my remaining strength, I pushed the flimsy wall of the house and it gave way. I managed to escape, sliding down one of the posts which supported the house, and I reached firm ground.

Luck was with me as the monsters were at the other side of the house, scrambling to get up the steps. I saw a path to the forest and I hobbled as fast as I could go, leaning on my pole. My leg hurt dreadfully, but by sheer will-power, I limped to a mighty tree which stood not far off, and using both hands and my healthy leg, I scrambled to the very top of the tree. Once there, I tied myself to the tree with my belt, and exhausted by my efforts and by loss of blood, which was pouring freely from the deep wound in my leg, I fell into a swooning half-sleep.

When I roused myself from sleep, it was already morning. Girls were climbing down from the houses with bamboo buckets balanced on their shoulders and they hurried for water. As they passed my tree, they pointed at me in what seemed to be astonishment, and some of them, crying out, went running back, possibly to bring help. And sure enough, soon a few young men came hurrying towards me. They took me down from the tree, carried me to the village, and laid me down again on the bed which I had abandoned the previous night. There were no traces of the crocodiles, everything was as it had been the evening before, even the wall through which I had escaped had been skilfully repaired. I did not know what to think. All the members of the house came running to me, and each one brought something for treating my terrible wound; one a pot of healing ointment, another a piece of cloth for a bandage. They leaned over me speaking in their language, as if they were saying something to me, but I could not understand them, and they apparently did not understand me. Their care, and also the way their hands were treating my wounds quite convinced me of their good will. And so I gave up, in hope that perhaps later I might learn of what had actually happened, and what fate had befallen my crew.

Then suddenly, the elder with whom I had exchanged greetings the evening before walked into the house where I lay. He had a bandage around his head, and he walked with the help of a cane. In an imperious voice he ordered those who had been tending me away, and he leaned over my leg. His face drew closer to my wound, almost as if he were sniffing it, and at the same time he muttered something which might have been an incantation. Gradually and with growing horror, certainty was rising within me. Yes, I have seen this before, I have experienced this before, I know the expression on this face! In rapid succession the pictures of my battle with the crocodiles flashed through my mind, and in that instant I knew why that old man had a bandage round his head! By sheer will power I managed to stop myself from fainting.

I shall not trouble the noble ear of my master with a detailed description of the course of that day. Your humble slave will confine himself to simply stating that at the first opportunity, just as soon as he was left alone, he slipped from the house and hobbled as fast as his legs would carry him to the river.

When I came to the river bank, I understood why they had left me alone. Not far from the village, on the other side of the bend in the river, I saw a throng of wailing women, their faces smeared with mud. They were mourning over a dead man, whom four strong men were laying to rest in a narrow skiff with a long bow, decorated with carved crocodile heads. It was evidently the skiff in which they carried their dead to their place of burial. And at that moment, I was convinced that I would recognize the young man who was being mourned – and with even greater effort I hurried to the spot where we had pulled our boat ashore the day before. I had stopped hoping that I would ever see my unfortunate crew again; I was certain that the very same fate which I had only just escaped the night before had caught up with them to the last man.

The boat was there. It was rocking in the rushes not far from the shore, within reach of my pole. Of course it was empty, all the merchandise was gone, but since I had resigned myself to the loss of my crew, how could I lament over the loss of property? It made it all the easier for me to pull the boat to shore and climb into it. I sat down on the floorboards, giving my mauled leg as much freedom as possible. I pushed off from the shore with my pole, and with a short prayer to Allah, I entrusted myself to the river's current.

It was an interminable voyage before the water carried me to the village where we had spent the night, one day before our arrival in that nightmarish place. The current was not strong and the boat caught on every treetrunk, ran aground on every shoal in the river. It cost me a tremendous effort to force my weakened limbs to move, so that I could free the boat. When I finally sighted the village, I was so exhausted that I urgently needed treatment and care. I entrusted myself to these people with grave misgivings. But I was relieved when I found a person there who understood and could speak a few words of our language with me. He showed the greatest sympathy and laughed as delightedly as a child when I described my escape to him. But he grew white with fear when he heard the word crocodile on my lips. He looked as though he did not understand it, and looked upstream fearfully whenever I uttered it. But all the greater was the care he gave my wounds, and searching for the words with difficulty, he assured me that it was only by a miracle that I had escaped.

It was some time before I recovered enough to be fit for further travel. This man then acted as my guide, and escorted me in safety all the way to my ship.

I parted from him and showered him with many gifts which he had never before seen in his life, and whose use he did not know. Then I gave the order for the anchor to be weighed at once, and although I was hardly able to move, I set sail with the remainder of my sailors and what was left of my goods. And so, taking advantage of a favourable wind, we sailed successfully through all the dangerous waters, and after several days' sailing, we reached home.

In closing, I should like to say a few words to my Noble Master as to what conclusions I draw from this adventure, whose consequences, I am sorry to say, will accompany me all the way to my grave. I believe that I spent the night in a place whose inhabitants were crocodiles. They took on the form of human beings during the day so they could all the more easily devour unsuspecting travellers and rob them of their wealth. I do not agree with those who believe that these creatures had two natures; evil and voracious during the night, and kind and welcoming in the day. On the contrary, I am convinced that their daytime kindness was a deception, and that all their thoughtfulness sprang only from their perverse love of the smell of my blood. That elder of theirs, in whose face I recognized that gigantic crocodile who had mauled my leg, gave me all the proof I needed.'

'May this pouch of gold serve as proof of the favour you have found with Us, Captain Hasan,' His Majesty declared, and he threw the story-teller his reward.

The Postponed
Career

The young student Su Mei-sheng came from a well–connected old family. His ancestors at one time had held high office, but in recent generations, the family had been on the decline and now lived in seclusion. Su Mei-sheng was an only son, and because he had showed great promise since his childhood, the family had placed all their hopes in him.

Unfortunately, Su frittered away his talents in frivolous amusements. For days on end he would wander with his friends from one tavern to another, drinking merrily. Instead of sitting in his study and preparing for his examinations by diligent study of the classical scriptures, he squandered his exceptional abilities in composing melancholy love-songs.

Once he and his friends were returning from some noisy frolic. They chatted merrily, their spirits high from the wine they had drunk, and they paid no attention to their surroundings. Suddenly an old monk with a clean-shaven head stepped up to them, holding an alms bowl in his hands. The young people began to mock him, saying that he had chosen badly, that he would get nothing from them, because whatever they might have had they had spent in the taverns. But the monk paid no attention to their words; he sought Su Mei-sheng with his stern eyes and said:

'An excellent career awaits this young man. He will attain high position and will restore the fame of his family.' Then, without waiting for the drunken company to recover from their surprise, he continued on his way.

His friends began to taunt Su Mei-sheng, saying that he had better bury himself in his studies at once, but Su cried:

'Leave me alone! If that prophecy is true, then it will be fulfilled no matter what I do. So why should I rush back to my studies?'

Some time went by. Though Su Mei-sheng spent most of his days among his carefree friends as before, the memory of the strange monk and his prophecy kept returning to him. Finally he made up his mind; why not try his luck and make his family happy. And so the next time the examination commissioner came to the district capital, Su decided that this time he would sit for them. He took no great pains with his preparations, relying on the monk's prediction. He prepared only the most important things, and set off to the district capital.

Late in the afternoon he arrived in a small town. He decided to spend the night there, for he would not arrive in the capital before the closing of the gates. So he found an inexpensive lodging, and because he was not accustomed to sitting about on his own, he went into the town to see if he could find some entertainment. In a remote corner near the town walls, he saw an immense estate. Above the grey walls rose the soft outline of many roofs and high pavilions, and amongst them all green plane-trees spread their soft shade. It was apparently the estate of some wealthy and noble family. The beautiful palace lured Su Mei-sheng, and when he came closer, he saw that the gates were open, and so he stepped right up to them and stared inside, full of curiosity. Evidently there was some sort of celebration taking place in the palace. There was activity everywhere, and many servants ran to and fro in the courtyards. The colourful bustle captivated Su and he stood at the gates staring at everything that was happening. A young girl came running out of the house beside him, shouting something merrily. But as soon as she caught sight of the unknown young man, she turned her face away shyly and ran back into the house. Her beauty caught Su's heart, and he remained standing there in hope that he might see her again. It did not occur to him how impolite it was to loiter outside a stranger's house.

Just then an old servant came out of the house and walked towards him. Su was already preparing his apology and about to leave, when the servant stepped up to him courteously and in the name of the master of the house, invited him inside. Su Mei-sheng did not hesitate and accepted the invitation gladly.

The interior of the palace, with its stateliness and luxury matched the impression created from the outside. Su was ushered into the Banquet Hall where the whole family was gathered. They were in the midst of a huge banquet in celebration of the birthday of the master of the house, Mr Hu, a high official in retirement. Su introduced himself and explained that he was in the town for just a short time; that he had stopped there on his way to the district capital, where he was going for the examinations. He apologised for having stood so rudely at the gates of the house, but he had been enchanted by the stateliness of the palace and the green trees. His hosts wished him great success in his coming examinations and invited him to their table. Soon the festivities grew lively once again, one cup of wine went round after the other, and the revellers amused themselves composing verses. Su soon won the admiration of all the company with his humour and his quickness. All of them grew more and more exhilarated, the wine did not decrease and when it grew late, the master of the house invited Su to spend the night.

'Our house would be honoured, were we able to extend shelter to such a gifted young man. Stay with us for as long as you please.'

So Su stayed. The family grew very fond of him, and after several days, the eldest son offered him the hand of his youngest sister in marriage; the shy beauty whom Su had spied that first evening in the courtyard. Su forgot the district

capital, he forgot the examining commissioner, and he accepted the proposal. They celebrated the marriage and from that time on, Su spent all his days in the company of his young wife and her family.

The days went by, he hardly noticed them. One day his father-in-law summoned Su and requested him to go and sell a family jewel for him in the town. It was a jade pendant of rare workmanship. His father-in-law apologized for troubling him with such a trifling matter, but, he explained, he had been waiting for some time for couriers from his estates who were to bring him money. Who knows what could have happened to them, they had been long delayed. He had decided to sell the jewel to tide him over until he received news of his couriers.

Su willingly set out to the market-place in the town to seek out an antique dealer. But he had no more than shown the jade pendant to the first antique dealer he came across, when the man whitened with fear and immediately called for the city guards to come and arrest Su. He was accused of theft. It turned out that the jewel belonged to the family of a noble official and had been stolen some time before. The official had circulated its description all over the region, and naturally every antique dealer kept his eyes open so he would not get involved in unpleasantness with the authorities. In vain Su explained that he had not stolen the jewel, that his father-in-law, Mr Hu, had given it to him. No one in the town knew of him, and Su had a difficult time explaining what he was doing there. If he had been going to the district capital to take the examinations, then why had he stayed in the town? Why, the examinations had ended long ago! In vain Su pleaded his innocence. He was imprisoned until the judge investigated the entire matter.

After many days Su was finally called to trial. Neither the judge nor any of the officials knew a Mr Hu who had a palace near the town walls. The suspicion against Su increased, and it looked as though there was no way of proving his innocence. In tears Su begged the judge to go with him to his father-in-law's house; he would explain everything. Su did not confess to the theft under torture, and his testimony remained the same. The judge could not discover any new evidence about the theft, and so eventually he consented to take Su to the home of Mr Hu. Su led them along the path that he had taken on his first walk through the town, but at the walls, where the spacious and impressive palace had stood, there was now only an abandoned heap of rubble. Weeds

grew high among the crumbling walls, the pond was overgrown with pond-weed and only the tall plane-trees stood in their places as before. There was not a trace of a living soul anywhere, let alone a noisy and wealthy dwelling.

Su did not know what to do. Now he was indeed lost, for no one would believe his story about the large and wealthy Hu family. What else could he do, but stick to his own story and repeat over and over again that he had spent many days in a wealthy palace where this pile of rubble now stood. The guards combed the area thoroughly, and in one remote corner, choked with weeds and cobwebs, they found a bundle of things that belonged to Su Mei-sheng. It was a meagre bundle and contained only those things necessary for his examinations. Because of this, the judge finally believed Su. He realized that Su had been tricked by foxes, and he let him go.

Exhausted and weary, Su returned to his native town. It was a long time before he recovered from the wounds he had suffered in prison under torture. He firmly resolved to give up his beloved diversions, and he even came to hate those merry drinking sessions with his friends. He spent whole days sitting in his study preparing for the next examinations. But as time went by, Su recovered his health and his strength returned. His sufferings faded from his mind, and so in spite of everything, he did not resist the lure of his merry companions, and now and then went out in the town with them.

One night as he was returning home he met an extraordinarily beautiful girl. Her eyes were wet with tears. Her light step and her beautiful face so attracted Su, that he spoke to her:

'Is there anything I might do to help you, dear young lady? Where are you going so late and all alone?'

The girl turned her tearful face away and quickened her step. But Su would not let himself be discouraged, and he caught up with her and insisted on an answer. Finally the girl told him that her name was White Jade, and that she had run away from her stepmother because she treated her unkindly. But she had run away so hurriedly that she had brought nothing with her and now she did not know what was to become of her. She did not even have a place to lay her head.

Su took a liking to the young girl and offered her shelter in his house. At first White Jade was reluctant to accept the invitation, but night was fast approaching and so she agreed.

'I do not know how I shall repay you for your kindness,

dear sir. Consider me, unworthy as I am, as your servant. I shall do everything in my power to fulfil your every wish.'

And so White Jade settled into Su Mei-sheng's study with him. She truly took care of him, but her beautiful pale face engaged Su's attention more and more, and again he grew forgetful of his studies; he laid aside his books and dust began to settle on them. He gradually stopped going out of the house at all; he neglected his friends and even his family. And on those rare occasions when he did go out, everyone was appalled by his appearance. He had sunken cheeks, a weary expression and he was withered away to half his former self. But he dismissed all advice and questions, saying that nothing was wrong with him, he was only working hard preparing for his examinations. He was living in some sort of trance, and he was wasting away noticeably day by day.

His situation grew more and more grave and his family gave way to despair. They were afraid that their only son, their only hope, would die before their eyes, without their being able to do anything to help him. In the midst of their great helplessness, someone advised them to invite a famous monk to their house. He was versed in things both natural and supernatural, and he alone might know what to do.

It was an old monk, his face was lined with wrinkles, and he walked with difficulty, supporting himself on his staff. But when he learned of Su's mysterious illness, he came willingly. Because Su refused to see anyone, the monk waited calmly until an opportunity came and Su went out. Then he

examined him from a distance, and said to Su's mother:

'Your son is in grave danger. His entire being is surrounded by a dark aura, which means that he is in the power of a vampire. His life hangs by a thread!'

The family was horrified. They called Su and tried to explain to him what the monk had revealed. But Su waved his hand and was not even willing to hear them out. He was certainly not going to be influenced by the words of a mad old monk. How could there be a vampire with him? After a great deal of persuasion, however, he relented and allowed the monk to go with him into his study and convince himself that there was no vampire there.

And so it happened. The monk strode directly towards the study, and Su walked slowly behind him. The monk threw open the door and saw a pale beautiful girl with black hair. The grace in her face, the depths in her dark, clear eyes, exceeded all mortal imagination. It was White Jade.

As soon as the girl saw the monk, she jumped up in fright and tried to flee. The monk drew his wooden sword and crossed her path. Then in a ringing cry, he commanded her to reveal herself in her true likeness. The beauty grimaced in fury, and all traces of grace disappeared from her face. Under the fixed stare of the monk her human skin began to crack. The high arching brows collapsed and split open, the clear deep eyes fell out on the cheeks. Where the tiny little nose had been, a long crooked green beak appeared. Little by little the human skin disintegrated completely, and in front of the astounded Su stood a hideous black monster.

Su fainted in horror. The monk continued to stare at the monster, exorcising it with magic words. Slowly the monster faded and gradually it slipped away until it vanished altogether. Then the monk parted from the family, assuring them that the vampire would never appear among them again.

After this experience, Su gave up his good-for-nothing life. At first, he turned away from the gay companions of his youth completely and immersed himself in his study. His family were overjoyed to see the change in him, but after a time they began to fear that he might become too solitary, so they encouraged him to go out and seek his friends and learn to laugh again. Finally the horror of the transformation of White Jade began to fade and Su found peace of mind. When the time came, he passed his examinations and in a short time, he attained the degree of doctor in the capital city. The road to his career now lay open, and indeed, until the end of his life, he held the highest offices in the empire.

A certain learned man, on hearing this story, declared: 'It is said that everyone reaches his goal, if it was foreordained, though he take the widest detours. It is interesting, though, that foxes, vampires and all strange beings in general search out those very ones who would avoid the direct path.'

The Rivals

In a deep valley in the mountains, there was a village where a young basket-maker, Manuel, whom they called Bold One, lived. He was a kind young man and people were fond of him, but then they began to avoid him and some even preferred to go out of their way in order to avoid meeting him. For a strange rumour had spread about him in the village.

Whenever people gathered together, either on the way to the sugar-cane fields, or on a visit to their neighbours, someone was certain to ask:

'Have you heard that someone has put a curse on Manuel the basket-maker?'

And another would join in:

'Poor Manuel. He will fall prey to an evil disease, or else he will be devoured by some monster.'

One of the older villagers would then add in a warning voice:

'If only that were all! If that evil disease once finds its way among us, it could establish itself here and pounce down on everyone who happens to come into its path.'

And yet no one knew where the rumour had come from. No one owned up to it, everyone had heard it from someone else, and so finally the villagers came to the conclusion that it had been brought by the 'evil wind', a messenger of the devil.

Eventually, when Manuel learned of it, he had his own opinion. He was certain that he had harmed no one, so no one had any reason to take his revenge on him. But he also knew that there was someone in the village who envied him and did not wish him well. He said to himself that the rumour must have been planted among the people by Jacinto, whom they called Indian Corn. Jacinto and Manuel for some time now had been competing for the favour of Paola, the most beautiful girl in the village, and she had been paying much more attention to Manuel lately. This so grieved and angered Jacinto, that he had already slandered Manuel several times. It seemed likely that Jacinto had made up the rumour so people would be afraid of Manuel, especially Paola.

Manuel was right. It did not occur to him that Jacinto was so corroded by envy and jealousy that he had committed an act for which no one in the village would have forgiven him. One Friday night he had secretly gone to a deserted place far away in the mountains. There, at midnight, he had planted three black candles and a piece of aromatic resin in the ground. He had laid Manuel under a curse and surrendered him up into the hands of evil powers.

For some time nothing unusual happened. To Manuel's great joy, Paola did not belong among the fearful, and she went on seeing him. And so Jacinto's suffering continued, and what was more, his conscience tormented him for the evil deed he had committed. But then he said to himself, half out of hope, half out of pity, that perhaps he had not performed the magic rite quite correctly.

Until one day, just before noon, a horrified scream rang out on the path to Paola's parents' house:

'The devil! The devil!'

In the next instant the woman who lived next door came darting into the courtyard, quaking and covering her eyes. Before she could describe what had happened, the gates suddenly opened of their own accord, and a high column of dust swirled up between them. In the middle of the dust something turned black and suddenly a left hand with long claws, all overgrown with stiff black hairs emerged from it. The hand groped in the air as though searching for something, reaching forward into the courtyard. But before the people could recover from their shock, the hand and the dust suddenly vanished and the gates slowly closed once again.

Jacinto was at home dozing on a mat in the shade of an overhanging roof of suger-cane leaves. He was awakened by a strange rustling sound, and looking up at the roof, he saw something moving there. It was a hairy black hand with long claws, fumbling through the leaves of the roof. Then it rose up, gave a short wave, an eddy formed around it and the hand vanished.

During that noon-time the hand appeared in many places throughout the village. Here it stopped in the door, there in a window; it reached over the low roofs, opening and closing its long fingers, as though it were searching for something and

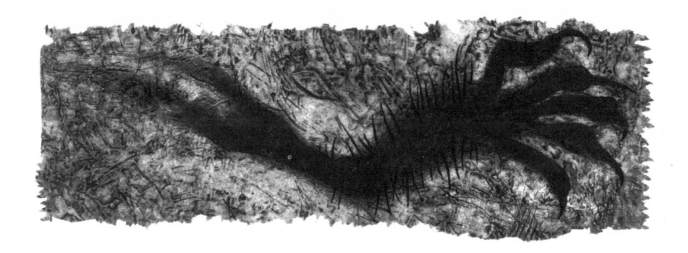

trying to catch it. But then it vanished and never appeared again. The villagers concluded that it had been looking for Manuel, but evidently had not found him, for he had not seen it and nothing had happened to him.

The people breathed a sigh of relief, but a certain uneasiness remained, even if they thought no more about the apparition. It was as if something invisible remained, walking the paths between the houses, searching for something.

A whole week went by and Manuel went off to the market in the nearby town with a few baskets and satchels. He had a good day, he soon sold everything he had brought to market and he still had time to stop to talk to his friends on the outskirts of the town. When twilight began to fall, Manuel, in high spirits after the diversion, tucked a flower in his hat, and with his satchel full of purchases, set off for home.

As he went, Manuel reflected that since the day when the hand and the evil wind passed through the village, he had only met Paola once for just a short time. Perhaps she had grown frightened of him, or perhaps her parents prevented her. Was it possible that the persistent Jacinto had finally won her favour? Manuel's high spirits vanished and he no longer hurried but trudged along slowly through the clear moonlit night deep in thought.

When he arrived at the village and passed the first house on the slope above the path, he thought he saw something white a little distance in front of him. He looked closer and saw a woman's figure with a white blouse and a long dark skirt and a shawl over her head. Paola is waiting for me, he thought, and his heart leapt with joy. But in the next moment he said to himself that he was probably mistaken, for it was much too late. But then she called him by his name and it was certainly

Paola's voice. Joyfully he ran towards her with outstretched arms, but Paola laughed and ran a little. When Manuel had almost caught up with her again, she called out, 'See if you can catch me, Manuel!' and ran on.

Thus they ran, Manuel almost catching up with Paola, and she laughingly evaded him again, until they passed Jacinto's house. Jacinto was not asleep, he was sitting on his mat under the roof and thinking that though his witchcraft had created a rift between Paola and Manuel, he had not succeeded in winning her. At that moment he heard footsteps and Paola's voice calling to Manuel. A violent jealousy came over him. Quietly he slipped out of the gate and set off after them.

The path twisted and turned among the gardens. Jacinto did not want to follow them too closely, and when at last they came to the bridge over the stream, they vanished from his sight. In a little while, Jacinto heard a horrified scream. The next instant he saw a figure in a white blouse, with a shawl over her head coming towards him over the bridge. Then he heard Paola's voice: 'Jacinto, Jacinto, come here to me!' Jacinto, frightened by the scream, and at the same time overjoyed at her calling, whispered: Paola! and ran towards her.

When he had run right up to her, the figure suddenly turned aside the shawl and instead of Paola, Jacinto saw a hideous face with a huge mouth and out-thrust fangs. Then a hand with long claws flashed before his eyes, with a scream Jacinto fell to the ground and knew no more.

Whoever was the first to go out the next morning found Manuel on one side of the bridge and Jacinto on the other side. Both were dead, their faces dreadfully mauled.

It turned out that the old people had been right. The devilish hand had brought the evil senguanaba into the village. It had apparently entrenched itself under the bridge, and no one knew in whose image it would again beguile people and then assault them.

'We shall probably have to tear down the bridge and build a new one somewhere else,' the villagers concluded.

The Path over
the Mountains

It was a sunny Sunday in spring, and two boys, the brothers Ivar and Kristoff, who lived in the seclusion of the valley, came over the mountains into the harbour town, sheltered by the cliffs of a fiord.

They strolled among the people dressed in their holiday best, and basked in the warm sun, which had finally begun to shine properly after the long winter. They stopped at the church, and listened to the music and watched the dancing. Finally they went to look at the harbour. They sat down on a pile of sacks and gazed at the ships, large and small, fishing boats and freighters floating calmly on the water, one tied up next to the other.

'I should like to have such a boat some day,' said Ivar. 'I would hire some sailors and sail far away.'

'I would go with you,' Kristoff added. 'Perhaps I could be helmsman. That would be better than leading cows to pasture.'

They lingered in the harbour all afternoon. They strolled from boat to boat, imagining what their boat would look like, and all the places that they would visit. Not until it began to turn a little chilly did they remember that they should have started on their return journey long before. They ran quickly through the town and began their climb into the mountains.

'We shall not return home before nightfall now,' said Kristoff.

'If we hurry, we shall make it to the pass while it is still light, and by then we shall see the lights shining in the windows down in the valley,' Ivar comforted him. 'And today it is clear, so our path will be lit up by the moon.'

The path wound up the hillside towards the mountain pass and on either side of it grew spruce and pine trees. From time to time between the trees, they could see the bare mountain silhouetted against the darkening sky on one side, and on the other the dark valley. In some places the path was washed away by water, in others thick roots stretched across it, and occasionally they had to go around or climb over boulders which seemed to have been thrust out by the forest. But the brothers knew the path well, and so they travelled quickly.

In a short time it grew quite dark, but because the moon shone brightly, they could travel almost as quickly as in daylight, even though they occasionally stumbled over rocks hidden by the long shadows of the trees. They had almost arrived at the pass when Kristoff caught his brother by the hand, stopped and said:

'Wait a moment, I think there is someone walking behind us.'

'You are probably just hearing things,' Ivar dismissed him. 'Why, we are going so quickly that someone would have a difficult time catching us up.'

'But perhaps we could wait a moment. Someone may have got lost and would be glad of our company. Listen!'

But they heard nothing and so they continued on their way. Only Kristoff lagged behind a little and now and again he would look around, for he was almost certain that every so often he heard the sound of stumbling footsteps coming from some distance behind them. Finally he stopped once more and called out to his brother:

'Now listen!'

And this time Ivar distinctly heard something like heavy footfalls coming from the darkness below them. But he laughed and said:

'That is probably a small rock-slide somewhere. Come along, so we can be home and get some sleep.'

But he had hardly finished speaking, when he saw that something was moving behind them at the turn in the path. It was not a human being. Way up among the tips of the pine trees, silhouetted against the starry sky, something huge and black was moving. It expanded, and then narrowed, it divided itself and then merged. It snorted loudly and stamped its feet dreadfully, and was quickly approaching along the path to the mountain pass.

Both brothers froze in terror, for the apparition was larger than the hugest bear, and they could scarcely expect anything good from such a creature. Then they heard that it was mumbling something to itself, and soon they distinguished the words:

'I smell a human being.' And in a little while: 'He's somewhere close by.' And then: 'Look for him, so we can catch him.'

The brothers took to their heels in flight. They ran as fast as their legs could carry them, but before long they heard a few heavy footfalls, and the loud snorting was quite close. They realized that they could not run away, and so they quickly took cover, one behind a thick juniper bush and the other behind a large rock. At that moment the apparition also stopped, and for a while there was silence. But then the voices rang out again:

'Is he really here somewhere?'

'I am sure I smell him.'

'And did you see him?'

'Yes, I saw him, but now he has gone.'

'But I still smell him somewhere close.'

'Here, I will have a look.'

The odd thing about it was that the voices were apparently talking to one another, as though there were several speakers, and yet they all sounded the same, as though it was the same voice.

Then when all was quiet again and nothing was happening, Ivar was overcome with curiosity, and cautiously he pulled the branches of the bush apart and looked to see what it was that was chasing them. He saw that it was a troll, a spirit of the mountains, 'the ugly troll', as he was called in the north. In fact, they were three trolls, except that they were indistinguishable from each other, they stood one pressed against the other, and each held on to the other's shoulder with a huge paw with long claws.

They had short, stout bodies on enormously long legs. They had three huge shapeless heads with flapping ears and they were as tall as the tips of the trees. In the light of the moon, they were as grey as rocks, straight black hair like brushes bristled out from their chins, long black beards like horse tails hung all the way to their knees. Their heads tottered and turned from side to side, and as they sniffed greedily, they wrinkled up their round, ball-shaped noses so that sharp white fangs glittered above their black whiskers.

Ivar's mouth grew dry with fear, but all the same he preferred to watch the trolls so that he could see what they were doing. Then he noticed that they were not in fact entirely alike. For only one of them had an eye. The other two had an empty eye socket in the middle of their foreheads. But that single shiny eye was as big as a saucer and it moved from side to side, its gaze falling on the bush where Ivar was hiding.

Now he has seen me, he thought and shook so much in fright, that the bush trembled. And at that moment he saw the long paw of the first troll reaching out towards him. Quickly he jumped up and ran to hide behind the rock where his brother was also trembling fearfully. The other two trolls began to grope with their paws, and they argued with each other:

'Have you got him?'

'I almost caught him, but now he has gone again.'

'You did not look properly.'

'He ran off somewhere downhill.'

'Then give me the eye, I will catch him.'

Then the first troll removed the eye, and handed it to the second. He inserted it in the hollow in his forehead and began to search around until his glance fell on the brothers' hiding place. Apparently they were not very well hidden, because the troll cried out: 'Now I see him!' and he reached out for them. But he reached into emptiness, because both brothers jumped away and ran off in different directions. The trolls burst out again:

'Did you catch him?'

'No, he ran downhill. Here, you catch him!' replied the middle troll, removing the eye and handing it to the third. He put it in place, looked around and caught sight of Kristoff, who was running up the hill. The troll growled in displeasure:

'You do not know how to look properly, why he is uphill. Here!' and he handed the eye back to the first troll. In the meantime, Kristoff had hidden behind a bush, so the troll did not see him, and he handed the eye to the last one again and said:

'He probably ran down the hill after all, I do not see him here.'

Then the middle one spoke out:

'Both of you have failed, I almost had him, give me the eye!' and he reached out his paw. But in his blindness, he struck the eye lying on the first troll's palm. The eye fell to the ground and rolled towards Ivar, who was looking to see where he could hide. Ivar nimbly caught it, and just to make sure, covered it quickly with his cap. The trolls began to quarrel:

'Did you catch him?'

'But you did not give me the eye.'

'Why, you took it!'

'No, you did not give it to me.'

'Nor to me.'

'Since you kept the eye yourself, at least catch that human.'

'I do not have it.'

Ivar realized that the trolls were now powerless, and he was so amused by their quarrel, that he burst out laughing.

All three trolls cried out:

'Hear that? He is here, hurry up and look!'

Then they fell silent and after a moment all three of them said together in horror:

'We have lost the eye!'

'Yes, you have lost it,' Ivar answered them. 'And I have it and you will never get it back from me.' He preferred to run a little distance away, though, because the trolls turned at once towards the voice and began to flail their arms about, groping for Ivar. Then the middle troll said:

'Give me my eye back at once, or you will be in serious trouble. I do not even have to catch you, all I have to do is just barely touch you, even with my beard, and you will instantly be turned to stone.'

'You shall not succeed!' Ivar cried cockily, seizing the eye and fleeing. But the trolls immediately set off after the sound of his footsteps, their beards flying. When they had almost caught up with him, he tried to swerve, but he tripped and fell. At that instant Kristoff ran out from his hiding-place and at once the trolls turned around and ran after him. But Kristoff stopped after a few steps, and the trolls lost track of both brothers. They stood for a long time without moving,

listening and sniffing all around, but the boys did not move a
muscle, they scarcely even breathed, so the trolls would not
hear them.

Meanwhile, far on the horizon the outline of the mountains
appeared as the sky began to grow light with the coming
dawn. The trolls grew uneasy and again called out:

'Please, give us back the eye, we cannot go back home
without it.'

'You are faster, you need not be afraid of us, so give us back
our eye.'

'Without it we shall die, and it is of no use to you.'

The boys did not reply. Meanwhile Kristoff had quietly
crept right next to Ivar. Then the middle troll said:

'Give us back our eye, we shall reward you handsomely. I
shall give you all the gold you can carry. Look!' and he began
to shake his long black whiskers, and from his whiskers pieces
of gold began to pour out with a ringing sound, until there
was a big shiny pile of them.

It was such an extraordinary sight that Kristoff whispered
into his brother's ear:

'What if we were to return the eye to them? We could buy the biggest ship there is with all that gold.'

But Ivar shook his head and replied in a whisper:

'It is ours anyway, wait and see.'

The sky above the horizon turned grey and then white. The trolls spoke out again:

'All that will be yours if you give us our eye, but hurry, before it is too late.'

They had hardly finished speaking, when light flashed over the mountains and the first morning ray of sun fell on the trolls. And in that instant they began to lose their shape, and before the sun had peeped over the horizon, three enormous boulders were standing across the path. They were as tall as the tips of the pine trees and they leaned one against the other, thickly overgrown with moss.

In Ivar's cap lay a smooth, round, white stone, but the pile of gold had vanished without a trace.

The House
in the Swamp

The fine, big house with the high roof was half-drowned in a swamp. Water surrounded it on all sides, and it was gradually being overgrown by rushes. The doors had fallen from their hinges and water birds could be seen nesting inside. A clear stream flowed into a clear, deep pool right behind the house. It was most strange. It was thought that the owners of the house had moved away suddenly far into another province. But their former maid lived in the village and she remembered how the house had flooded, and when asked would willingly tell her story:

'Not a soul goes to the house of Mr Shichiro today, and everybody avoids it. But in those days, when there were young people living there, visitors were calling every day. It was a very hospitable family, and Mr Shichiro, although a little severe, was a kind person at heart, and the mistress was goodness itself. And if anyone should say that what happened was my fault, there is no truth in it at all.

This is what occurred. At that time, of course, the swamp was not there – for who would build a house in a swamp – there was only the stream and the pool, and the stream was full of fish. The young mistress had just given birth to a son, and I had a great deal to do, what with the cooking and taking care of the household, and so I was glad when someone came to visit me in the kitchen and talk while I worked. Summer had just begun, and a dear little boy began to come to visit me; he might have been about eight years old, and even so he was quite small for his age.

The boy came almost every second day. He always slipped into the kitchen and sat a while and chatted just like an adult. He asked a great deal about the master's family, about the mistress and the little one, even about the house, how did it

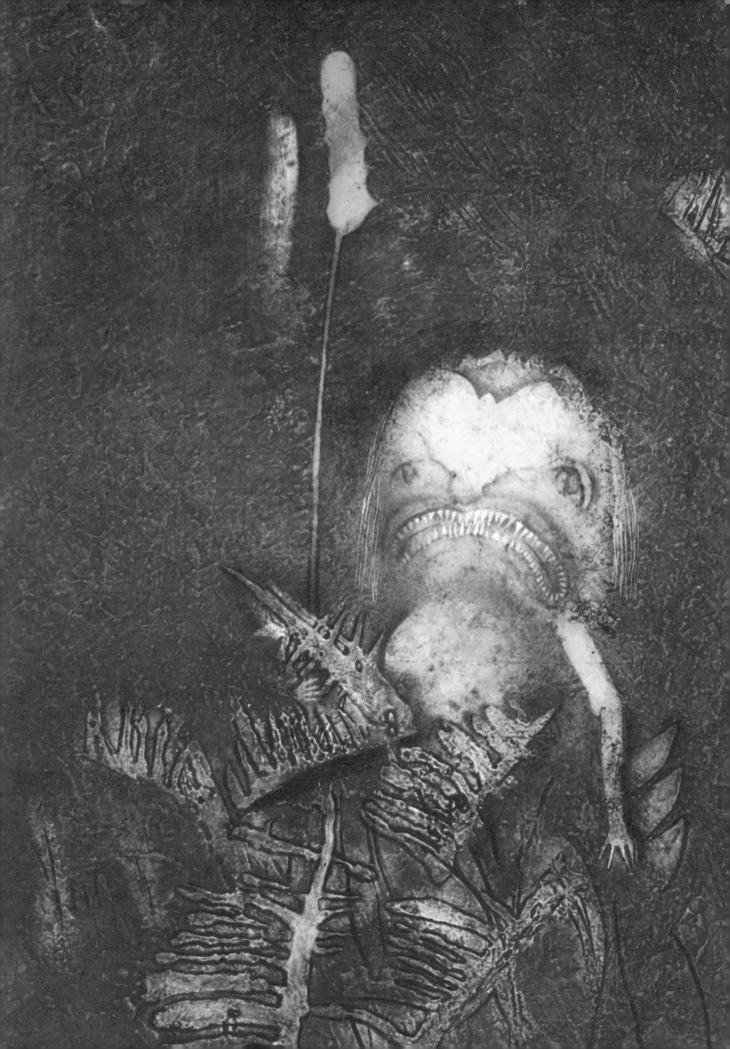

look inside, how many rooms it had, well, virtually everything. Almost every time he visited me he brought a fine fish which he said was from the source of the stream – he was a dear boy. I found it odd that I did not know where he came from. I knew that he was not from our village, for I would have known him, so perhaps he came from the neighbouring one. When I asked him about it, he laughed and said that he actually lived quite close. We were almost neighbours, he said, and somehow he always avoided the question. I suspected nothing at that time, except that I felt uneasy because I never saw him coming or going.

Once, when I was talking with the boy while I cooked, he begged me to let him into the house, because he would like to see it and he would like to see the little baby, too. This seemed to be going a little too far, and so I cut him short and told him that it was impossible. We really did not know him, and the master would certainly be angry. It was evident that he was very sorry for he almost burst into tears. He looked sad and sat without a word, then he blurted out: 'Very well then,' picked himself up and was gone.

I felt that I had hurt his feelings, which I had not wanted to do, so I ran after him quickly to explain. There was no sign of the boy. I looked everywhere, wondering where he had gone, and then I saw a little figure waddling towards the stream. But he looked entirely different. He was all green, his little body was half human and half frog and his hands and feet were webbed. He had something like a turtle shell on his back, and there was a little hollow with splashing water in his head. The creature was a water goblin, a kappa. I recognized him at once from stories I had heard people tell, although I had never seen one before. As I stood staring at him, he turned around, smiled sadly and waved at me. Then he hopped into the pond, the water splashed, and he was gone.

So the boy was not really a boy at all, but a kappa, and instantly all the mysteries that had surrounded him were clear. I grew afraid that he might harm the little one, but then I remembered how dear and kind he had been, and so I preferred not to tell anyone for the time being and I waited to see what would happen next.

At first nothing occurred. The boy did not come to visit me again. I missed his conversation, but as he was not a human being, I was glad that he left us alone.

After about a month, as I was going upstairs to fetch something from the attic, something flashed by me in the darkness on the stairs. Scarcely had I looked around before it

151

was gone, but I recognized the kappa. From that time on, I met him in the house all the time – on the stairs, in the halls, in the closets, in the attic, everywhere. But he always appeared so suddenly that he frightened me every time, and it began to make me nervous. I never did find out what he was actually doing there, because he vanished immediately. I never had a chance to speak to him. Finally, I could stand it no longer and I told the mistress about it, but she did not believe me and laughed that young girls are always afraid of something.

Then it happened. One day at noon, I had been to the well for water, when I heard the mistress scream in horror from inside the house. Then the master's furious voice rang out: 'What do you want here, you strange boy?' Then I heard the sounds of shouting and the banging of doors, and then the master again cried out: 'So you are a kappa? Well just you wait, I shall teach you a lesson for annoying people!' I saw the master catch the kappa on the verandah. He knocked him down, and the water from the kappa's head spilled out. Then the master untied his belt and tied the kappa into a little knot. For a while he stood towering over him, apparently not knowing what to do next. Then he growled: 'I shall teach you a lesson!' and he went into the house.

The kappa lay there pale-faced and trembling and you could see that he was very ill. He had lost all his strength when the water spilled out from his head. I felt sorry for him, although I did not know what he had done. But I was angry with him for frightening me all the time. Then I saw that he was straining with all his might. He twisted himself, and panted hard, and then his neck began to stretch. It kept growing longer and thinner, and before I knew it, that head on its long neck was in the bucket of water which I was carrying from the well. I screamed in fright, and dropped the bucket. At that moment, the master ran out of the house, brandishing a hefty stick, but it was too late. The kappa took a little water onto his head, freed himself from his bonds, jumped up, scurried to the pond and disappeared into it.

The master was angry because the kappa had escaped. He had wanted to thrash him because he had badly frightened the mistress. In the heat of the afternoon, she had dozed off a little, and when she awoke, she saw the kappa leaning over the baby, inspecting him closely. Who knows what he intended to do to him? The master said that the kappa would not come back, for he would be afraid of getting a thrashing. But just in case, he would have a fence built around the pond, and if the kappa did come, I was to call him at once.

That evening as the moon rose, the kappa cried out:

'You have treated me shamefully and you had no reason to do so. That I came to visit you? Why, we are neighbours! You really should have come to visit me, as is polite, because I was here first and you moved in. I thought that you probably did not know about me, and so I came to see how you lived. But I see that you are not pleasant neighbours, and so I do not want you here.'

It all sounded rather ominous, but the master was not afraid of him. He laughed and said: 'Go away if you do not like us, and leave us alone.' The kappa replied: 'We shall see!' and sank back into the pond.

From that time on the kappa never showed himself in our house again, nor did he emerge from the pond, but we no longer fared as well as before. The master should not have taunted him, because strange things began to happen. First our well was stopped with mud. They had hardly cleaned it out, when I went out into the courtyard one morning and found a huge puddle, although it had not rained. I tried to wade through it, but I sank to my knees in mud. The master said that the water from the stream was probably seeping into the courtyard, and he had a little rill dug, but it was no use, the water lay in the courtyard.

One night, a terrible noise rent the air, and the whole house swayed. We thought it was an earthquake, but it turned out that the posts supporting the house were undermined by water and the house sank about a foot into the ground. Frogs and toads began to crawl over the verandah. A swamp began to form under the verandah and bulrushes grew in it. The swamp grew larger and larger, until we had to walk from the house to the path over a wooden foot-bridge.

It was clear that this was the kappa's revenge. The people in the village felt sorry for us, and wondered how to outwit the kappa, but he never showed himself again. The swamp grew and grew and the floor in the kitchen began to be damp all the time. When the path became flooded, people grew frightened and began to say that the kappa would flood the entire village. They avoided us. When the master or the mistress went into the village, no one spoke to them, and finally they complained to the authorities. The master could no longer bear it, he took his family, left the house and moved somewhere far away. I do not know where they went, except it was a place far from water. Then the swamp stopped spreading, but the house is slowly sinking, and I would not be at all surprised if the kappa were living in it now.'

153

From the Notebook of Dervish Abdullah

In the name of God most merciful and all-compassionate! A dervish does not reap nor does he sow, he lives relying on the infinite mercy of God, which has no end and no boundary. He does not suffer hunger, as long as he walks through lands where God-fearing people dwell, and he does not fear for the morrow even among those who do not know God, for who would harm a person who has nothing and who harms no one? Not even in the desert does thirst torment him, for he is able to find springs of fresh water; for these reasons, even I, simple dervish Abdullah, set off on my travels at the beginning of this year's summer without apprehension and without anxiety. I went in the direction of the southern mountains, partly because I would avoid the dust of the valley paths, and partly driven on by my thirst for knowledge. For I had made up my mind to visit Madinat al-Kufara, a dwelling-place of non-believers, of which I had heard many tales.

I started in that direction not without fear, but my faith in the infinite mercy of God was stronger than my apprehension, and I believed that my dervish clothing would protect me among these savages.

The journey went by without mishap and I was soon bidding farewell to the last Moslem colony in that area. I searched for someone who knew the Kafirs and who might give me some advice. I found one man who knew someone on the other side of the mountains. He did all he could to dissuade me from going there but in the end he said: 'I see that your decision is irrevocable and it would be of no use to warn you of what awaits you in that land. So do as you wish, and I shall do the only thing I can.' Then he told me the name of a man he knew, handed me a small wooden box and added these words: 'When you meet him, show him this box, and Inshallah, it will be your safeguard. But do not open the box yourself, and above all beware of losing it. If that were to happen, I do not know what might save you.'

I thanked him and tucked the box away carefully. The following day I struck out into the mountains.

At the beginning all went well, for I was walking along sheep paths, but later the wide valley narrowed and I was forced to wade through bogs and around forest streams and scramble up steep precipices when I arrived at their sources. Next there came a chain of mountain plateaux. I had to spend several nights shivering with cold in mountain caves, and I found no food. My own supplies were scanty, and at times I nearly fainted from hunger. Finally on the fifth day, I crossed a wide mountain pass and a green valley, open to the south, spread out before me. It took me a day before I came to green pastures and there I saw the first Kafirs. They were tall, slender people, dressed in clothes of rough fabric. They were grim and forbidding, but not openly hostile. When I turned to them for assistance, they offered me sheep's milk and cheese, and gave me enough food to last me on my journey down into the valley.

Shortly after I parted from them, I was surrounded by a group of Kafirs who looked like robbers, which indeed they were. They obstructed my path, and threatened me with sharp knives. Then they tied my hands behind my back and drove me in front of them. When I protested against their violence, they merely laughed and tauntingly repeated my words, obviously not understanding me.

I was already regretting that I had not listened to my host, but I did not suspect that this was the least of my sufferings!

They took nothing from me, and so I did not lose the box. They drove me on with kicks and blows and they allowed me no rest until they had driven me into their city. I had to smile to myself when I reflected that I was arriving like a shackled slave in the city that I had wished to visit of my own free will.

They led me through the city gates and through narrow streets between houses built of rocks placed loosely, one upon the other. They forced me on until I stood in front of the residence of the ruler of that city. It was not much different from the rest of the houses. It was larger, and a shelter stood in front of it where a sullen man, smoking a long pipe, sat on a bench covered with furs. My guides pushed me down on my knees before him, and they bowed deeply saying something to him. In a curt voice the man would interrupt them every

155

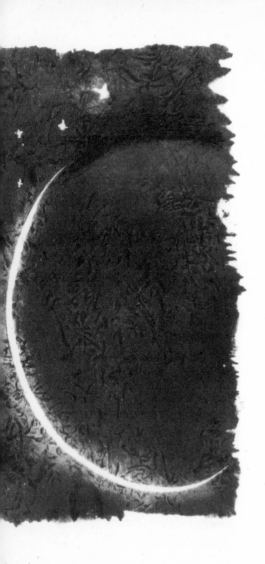

now and then, and at last he turned to me and said something. One of the men kicked me in the back and I fell on my face. When I raised myself, I began to cry out the name of the man who had been commended to me by my host on the other side of the mountains. My captors burst out laughing and repeated the name after me, for they thought I was pleading for mercy. Their ruler, however, interrupted them and repeated the words himself. I frantically began to indicate that yes, that was the name which I had wanted to say. The ruler then sent someone to bring the man to him.

After a while, a man who was even taller and more slender than the rest approached, and he spoke to me in Persian, asking what I wanted of him. Joyously I began to tell him how a certain friend of his had sent me to him, and I mentioned the box. The man turned to the ruler of the city and said a few words to him. Apparently he was ordering my hands to be freed, because before long I felt that someone was cutting my bonds. My hands were wooden and I could not gain control of them. But after a while I recovered enough to pull the box from my bosom and show it to the man. He took it, weighed it in his hand, opened it, and raising his hand high into the air, showed it to the rest of the people. Loud cries of wonder spread through the group, and instantly I felt that my position among these people had changed. They began to look at me differently, with a certain respect in their narrow eyes. Then the man restored the box to me, and after first requesting permission from the ruler of the city, led me away with him to his house.

I spent several weeks there and he treated me quite well. He fed me and did not prevent me from my prayers. By that time, I had learnt a few words of their language, and I tried to show my friendliness to them. No one ever spoke amiably to me. When they spoke amongst themselves, they appeared to be cheerful and expansive, but they only revealed their sullen side to me.

Then one day the man who had a friend on our side of the mountains and who was now my host, came to me and said:

'No stranger is allowed to come into this city, and should he come, he is not allowed to leave here alive. Up till now, that box which you brought with you has saved you. If you had arrived without it, we would have thrown you into the Tigers' Pit. As it is, you will only have to walk through Serpents' Gorge.'

I was greatly alarmed and asked him what that meant. The man replied:

'Do not inquire prematurely, for you will learn everything when the time comes. And know that I will do everything in my power to save you. Not that you matter to me, but out of respect for my friend who sent you to me.'

I was very frightened and I began to be preoccupied with the thought of escaping, but I soon realized that I could not succeed without outside help, for the inhabitants of that city did not let me out of their sight by day or night, and followed my every step. I recalled the words of my host and I assumed that he had implied the possibility of escape. However, when I hinted of my intention to him, he told me that I was a coward like all Moslems, and that he would throw me into Tigers' Pit himself if I should try to do so.

'I promised you that I would save you, but that does not mean that I shall support your cowardice,' he said to me. 'You can be happy if you escape Tigers' Pit; but you will not escape Serpents' Gorge. Now is the third quarter of the month. When the new quarter comes, they will elect the king in Serpents' Gorge. And then we will send you there.'

Soon the day arrived. The whole city had been preparing for weeks, and alas, I was to be the principal figure! On the eve of that day they had presented me with a lavish supper and offered me bottles of strong liquor. I could not swallow a morsel and I scarcely wet my lips with the brandy, although I should have liked to get intoxicated, heedless of God's prohibition. The following morning, just after dawn, a throng of maidens dressed in white came to the house. They took me amongst themselves, and singing and dancing all the while, they led me through the streets of the city to the house of their ruler. Only there did I meet my host again, and I was still counting on his help.

At a sign from the ruler, he spoke to me in the Persian language, telling me that on his intercession, and thanks to my being the holder of the box, I had been granted a favour such as very few strangers are granted: I would not be thrown to the tigers, but would be allowed to prove my courage and walk through Serpents' Gorge. I would be a substitute for the most beautiful virgin in the city, and I would be their representative during the voting for the king of the serpents. Thus he spoke, explaining the hidden significance of that ceremony to me. I, however, grasped only the danger that threatened me, and I concentrated my thoughts with difficulty. Finally he added in a voice just as strong, though now he was speaking to me personally:

'I see that you are afraid and so my advice will be of no great

157

value. I promised to help you, however, and I must do so. No one among these people understands Persian, and for that reason I am able to tell you that your box contains the coronation jewel of the serpent king. It is a large emerald and you were forbidden to look at it. It is well that you did not do so for you would not withstand it. You would gaze for so long into its brilliant light, that your sight would lose its sharpness and your will to live would be broken. But now pay careful attention: You will enter the gorge at the moment when it will still be covered in shade and the snakes, if they are not sleeping, will be stiff with night chill. Go quickly and be careful not to step on them nor to alert them with too much noise. If you hurry, you will walk to the end of the gorge before the sun's rays touch its floor. Then you are saved. There will be people awaiting you and by a different route will lead you ceremoniously back into the city, from which you shall go forth as a free man. But should you delay, the warmth of the sun will wake the snakes and they will attack you. Then you will have one chance: open the box and throw its contents to the snakes. After that it will not matter very much whether you step on them or not; the snakes will decide for themselves whether they will let you through without harming you.'

Having said this, he turned away. Then they set me into a litter which was standing there in readiness, and with rapid steps they carried me to the escarpment not far from the city. When they placed the litter on the ground, I saw before me a

chasm in the rocks which formed the entrance to Serpents' Gorge.

A throng of maidens dressed in white continued to dance around me, and the sombre beating of drums rang out. I turned back to look at my guides, but I saw the shiny blades of knives, and my host, who was standing not far off, made a sign with his eyes that I should waste no more time, for the sun was already above the horizon. And so, with a sigh, I set off, touching the box which I carried with me in my bosom.

The first section of the path through Serpents' Gorge was passable and I could walk through it at a rapid pace. There was not a snake in sight, perhaps they were hidden in holes beneath the boulders. But then the gorge narrowed, and its cracked walls full of dark holes were almost touching my sides. Here and there I saw a snake curled up beside the path on which I trod, or else hanging unconscious from the ledges in the cliff above my head, as they stared at me with glazed eyes, but none of them made the slightest move, and so my fear of them gradually faded.

Suddenly the gorge veered sharply to one side and a wider place appeared, whose walls were illuminated by the sun. I froze; from every chink in that rockface a huge snake was slithering down towards the floor of the gorge, every one of them stared at me, each one lashing out his forked tongue. I could not tear my eyes away from that picture, and I stopped paying attention to where I trod. Then in horror, I discovered that I was placing my feet just a thumbnail's distance from the bodies of no less terrible snakes that were laying about everywhere. I gave in to a sudden impulse and broke into a run. I ran and the rocks rolled beneath my feet, they struck one another and bounced against the walls, and the whole gorge was alive with their echoes. Suddenly the snakes were everywhere, on the walls, in front of me, behind me; they swayed their erect bodies, they hissed and they puffed out their necks. I saw the end of the gorge in front of me, and I also saw that the entire surface of the path before me was alight in the rays of the sun, and that from everywhere, more and more snakes came slithering forward. It was as if a forest of snake heads and bodies had suddenly grown up in front of me, and from each of those heads came such a loud hiss that my head began to whirl and my ears buzzed. Fascinated by their fixed stares, I walked closer and closer, and suddenly I stopped feeling that I was walking at all, I felt as though something was carrying me forward towards those rigid, glittery eyes, closer to those ghastly teeth. And so I was moving towards my own destruction, and my feeling was just like that of an idol worshipper who is sacrificing himself on the altar of his idol.

But Allah reminded me of His eternal presence and before my eyes appeared the most holy of His Names. I came to my senses at the last moment, when I was scarcely more than an open palm's distance from the most terrible of those dreadful cobras. He was rocking his head slowly from side to side, and in his eyes glowed the certainty that I would become his victim. With lightening speed I reached into my bosom and drew out the box. The instant the snakes caught sight of it, they began to hiss so loudly that it echoed like a gust of wind in a blizzard, and all around could be heard the dry rustling of their slithering bodies. I opened the box, and without looking inside it at all, I groped about with my fingers for the cool stone which was in it, and with a mighty swing I hurled it far away from me. And then with arms outstretched like a sleep-walker I stumbled forward, heedless of the snakes whose bodies I could feel beneath my feet.

But the snakes paid no attention to me. All of them, one on top of the other, were slithering swiftly to the spot where the stone had landed, they slashed about with their teeth, wounding one another. I ran to the mouth of the gorge and only stopped when I discovered that there were no longer any snakes around me. I still heard them everywhere, and I could not believe my eyes. Then I turned around and saw that the snakes were milling in a horrible cluster. The largest snake raised his head, and between his teeth glittered a huge, golden, fiery emerald.

For a moment I gazed on, and then I noticed that I was being surrounded by Kafirs who were bowing to me and paying me homage. Exhausted, I sank into their arms and I allowed myself to be put into the litter, and carried away to the city.

Everyone in all the city was dancing and laughing. But I had had enough of it all, and I only longed to return to a civilized country where kind and peaceful people live, and where snakes did not elect their king, but danced toothless in the market-place to the tune of an Indian fakir's flute.

They did not detain me, and so I soon descended into the lowlands from which, sometimes alone and on foot, sometimes on a camel with a caravan, I returned to my native country.

I have had enough of wandering – I have seen all too much. May God grant that I live out my days in the quiet shade of a monastery.

The Orphan

Somewhere in the lands beneath the Himalayas, it happened that in one village more girls were born than boys. They all married and went away, and there was no one to till the fields and tend the cattle. In a land where there are few men, tigers and wolves multiply, cattle die, and poverty grows, poverty which soon multiplies so that it feeds people from the same bowl. The fields fall fallow, for not even the most fertile soil will bear ears of corn without a ploughman's share. And the ploughshare rusts in the shed, because there is no one to guide it with a manly hand.

Once a child, hardly more than a babe, walked through that countryside. Perhaps it was looking for members of its family in that village, or else chance had guided its steps – it found no family, though, and there was no one to beg from, for they were all no more than beggars. So there was nothing left for the child to do but walk vainly through the dust in his bare feet, and look for shelter under the spreading trees in the burial-ground where it could sleep. The dead are not evil, the child said to itself, and what worse things could happen to me amidst all this misfortune? And it calmly lay down in the burial-ground, unmindful of snakes, hyenas or even ghosts.

And so the night passed, and nothing occurred to disturb its dreams. It probably dreamed of merry sisters and brothers or bowls full of food, and most certainly of its mother, how loving she was and how she was combing its hair, for the child smiled in its dreams and reached out its arms.

Then at that hour when it is hard to decide whether the night still lingers or whether day is beginning, at that hour when the stars have not yet faded from the sky and yet we begin to sense the coming of the sun, two evil demons settled in the branches of the tree above the child – a rakshasi and a rakshasa.

'What are you doing here?' demanded the rakshasi. 'The night belongs to me, according to the agreement we made.'

'I know our agreement better than you, for I came at dawn. It is you who is breaking our agreement, because it is not night any more.'

'How is it not night when the stars are shining in the sky?'

'Just look to the east. Do you not see the rays of the sun? Since when does the sun shine at night?'

'Even if it were day, the body which is laying here below us does not belong to you. We agreed that you will eat the dead that are lying about unguarded in the daytime, while the living that I find lying in the fields at night belong to me. And this child is living, look, it is smiling.'

'That it is smiling is no proof,' said the rakshasa. 'Did you not ever see the smile on the face of a victim of the plague? The fact that it is lying in the burial-ground, that is the main thing. Do the living lie in burial-grounds?'

'And even if it were a dead body, it would still not belong to you. For our agreement took that into account. Look, it is a boy, and all boys belong to me.'

'How can you say that it is a boy? Why, it is wearing a skirt! And do you not see the long curls? It is a girl, and you cannot deny that by right, girls belong to me.'

'Even if it were a girl, it is night, so it belongs to me!'

'Even if it were night, it is a live body so it belongs to me!'

'Even if that body were living, it is a boy, and all boys belong to me by right!'

'Even if it were a boy, it is no longer night, but day, so you cannot deny my right to it!'

'Even if it were day, it is a live body lying in the open. And I have the right to live bodies!'

'Even if it were a live body, it is a girl. So this is how you wish to observe our agreement, by falsehood?' the rakshasa burst out screaming.

'Do not scream at me, because you and not I are the one who is breaking our agreement. And what is more, you are nothing but a bald-headed carcass-eater!'

'If I am a carcass-eater, what are you, you violator of homes?'

'I am a violator of homes? No, to you nothing is sacred, you turn every law inside out, eternal and temporal!'

'And which one of us does not uphold agreements?'

'Why you, of course, who else?'

'I see that we are not going to agree,' the rakshasa finally decided. 'We shall have to turn to the judge to settle our quarrel for us. He will analyze our cause according to the laws and we shall see who is right, whether you or I.'

Having agreed on this, they went to the judge so that he might put the matter right. But what did the child do in the meantime? It awoke, stretched, yawned – and set off back into the village to try to find something to eat and appease its gnawing hunger.

Meanwhile the rakshasa and the rakshasi came to the wise judge, who was responsible for the upholding of the laws in that country. They explained their cause to him, the judge listened and then declared:

'I have been appointed here to be the guardian of the laws and my duty is to see that everyone is given his rights, regardless of whether he be human or demon. Your disagreement appears somewhat unclear to me. I hear of some sort of contract which you concluded, and I cannot fully grasp its meaning. 'You,' he turned to the rakshasa, 'state that according to the agreement, you have the right to devour every body that you find in the daytime?'

'Yes, judge,' said the rakshasa. 'Every body which I find during the day belongs to me.'

'You, on the other hand,' the judge turned to the rakshasi, 'declare that every live body which you find in the fields is your property?'

'Yes, judge,' said the rakshasi. 'As you yourself will admit, I am in the right.'

'One moment,' said the judge, 'the argument is not yet settled. As I understand your words, each of your rights is qualified by yet another stipulation, and that is the sex of the body in question.'

'Yes, indeed, judge,' said the rakshasa. 'And because it is quite evident that it is a girl in question, the body without doubt belongs to me.'

'Your cause is confused,' the judge found, 'although your intentions for making the agreement were undoubtedly to fairly divide all the bodies which you find between you. Now if I understand what you have told me correctly, to you,' he turned to the rakshasi, 'belong only living males which you find in the fields at night, while to you,' the judge said to the rakshasa, 'all the dead females which you find in the daytime. As you yourselves find, many cases are left which cannot be decided according to your agreement.'

'The body which we found, however, clearly does not

belong among such cases,' said the rakshasa. 'Because it was day and it was clearly a matter of a dead girl.'

'On the contrary,' said the rakshasi, 'it was night, and the body was a live boy.'

'Does a boy wear a skirt? Do the living lie in burial-grounds? Does the sun shine at night?' the rakshasa interrupted her.

'One thing is certain, that stars do not shine in the daytime,' said the rakshasi, 'and it is just as certain that the dead do not smile in their dreams. And as far as that skirt is concerned, what makes you so sure that that tattered rag which that body had around its hips was a skirt?'

'I see,' said the judge, 'that your argument is not easy to solve. Today there are many orphans whose hunger renders them neither dead nor alive, and they are so wretched that they tie any sort of tattered rag about their loins to cover their nakedness. In such a case it is difficult to decide whether it is a girl or a boy. And what is more, if they have no one to put them to bed at night, you can readily find them at daybreak sleeping in the burial-ground. And so the following is my ruling on the case: Each of you will take a gold piece and lay it next to the head of that body. If it is still lying there at noon and the coins are untouched, the matter is clear; the body is dead and belongs to the rakshasa. If it rises and takes the coins, you must wait to see how it disposes of them. Should it buy boy's clothing, it is a boy and by rights belongs to the rakshasi. But should it dress like a girl, and if it is found lying in the burial-ground by day, it is the rakshasa's and he can dispose of it according to the provisions of your agreement. But until all this is made clear, the body belongs to neither of you, and neither of you must touch it.'

'That is a fair judgement,' both demons agreed. 'Only in this way can we attain our rights without a quarrel.'

And with many thanks they parted with the judge and returned to the burial-ground.

The way was long, and before they arrived, it was night again. The child meanwhile had gone from one house to the other, but it found no one who would give it shelter for the night. So it returned to the burial-ground and laid itself down to sleep under the same spreading tree. Hardly had it fallen asleep when both rakshases came and each of them laid a gold piece beside the child's head, one on either side. Then they settled in the branches of the tree to wait and see what would happen.

When the morning dew fell, the child awoke, stretched,

yawned – and what did it see? On either side of its head lay a heavy gold piece. It did not consider long, but took both the gold pieces and ran off towards the village.

'That does not mean anything,' said the rakshasa. 'We must wait to see what it buys with the money.'

'The judge decided fairly,' the rakshasi agreed. 'But you will see that it is a boy and that he will buy boy's clothing. Then he will be mine!'

It was a boy and bought himself boy's clothing. But he was poor no more and the people of the village took him in. They sent him to teachers so that he could learn the sciences and become a wise man. And when he became wise, he bought a house and a field in that village, he enhanced the house, and he made the village famous. He had his own household, a beautiful wife and healthy, happy children.

And he never slept in the fields again, and he came to the burial-ground only after many years of a happy and contented life.

Except that the rakshasa and rakshasi were no more. They had died of hunger.

The Leopard
Man

There was once a young man who made up his mind to become the greatest hunter of his tribe. He practised throwing his hunter's spear, and he learned to stalk animals with great expertise, but somehow bad luck dogged his footsteps. When he went hunting, he had little success, and when he did manage to catch something the other young men of the tribe laughed at him because they always brought home more than he.

He was a handsome young man and more than one village maiden would have been happy to become his wife, but what father would give his daughter to such a failure! It seemed that fate had destined the young man to be a loser. He felt that he would live alone all his life, until one day, his wise grandmother advised him to go to the neighbouring village to visit the famous witch-doctor.

'Perhaps your bad luck is caused by the cunning and malice of forest spirits. I think that the witch-doctor will know what is to be done, and he will help you,' she said.

The young man felt that there was some hope for him, so he set off to see the witch-doctor taking gifts with him.

The witch-doctor received the gifts graciously, and asked what he could do to help him.

'I should like to become a famous hunter, so I could hunt every sort of animal,' said the young man.

'You would succeed if you learned to trace the animals and handle a spear accurately,' said the witch-doctor.

'I have already done so,' said the young man, 'but bad luck seems to stick to me like a shadow. Perhaps I have angered the spirits of the forest – no matter what I do I am always the least successful of the hunters of my tribe. I cannot even take a wife.'

'I know only of one remedy,' said the witch-doctor, 'but it is extremely dangerous. First I must know what you want to hunt, and how firm is your resolve to succeed. If you hesitate or are the least bit frightened, I can do nothing for you.'

'I want to hunt all the animals there are,' said the young man, 'and I want to win a bride. I am resolved to do everything you suggest, I am afraid of nothing in this world.'

'I know of many brave warriors and skilful hunters,' said the witch-doctor, 'but everyone of them has hesitated when I proposed what I am offering to you.'

'If they are such brave warriors and skilful hunters, why have they come to you for help? I cannot afford to hesitate,' said the young man.

'They are all afraid,' continued the witch-doctor, 'of at least one thing: themselves.'

'Themselves?' the young man questioned in astonishment. 'Animals do not fear me because they sense my misfortune, and the young men of the tribe mock me. And if I were to become a skilful hunter, I would not stand against myself with a weapon in my hand. Why should I be afraid of myself?'

'By my questions I had hoped that you would reflect upon your wish, but I see that I shall achieve nothing. Very well, I shall arrange that you become the greatest hunter in the land. If you do not grow frightened of yourself, you will be content and you will fare well. But should you discover what it means to be afraid of yourself, I do not know who will help you. For there is a remedy against every evil, against every force; only against oneself are there neither forces nor powers,' said the witch-doctor.

Then he gave the young man powerful herbs to drink and put him into a deep sleep in which he saw more than when wakeful and heard voices which the wakeful do not hear.

When the young man awoke from his sleep, the witch-doctor said to him:

'Return to your village and live as you have always lived. Do not go out hunting with the rest of the young men, only go when you know when you should go. You will be the most successful hunter of all, but I fear that you will not escape the knowledge of what it is to be afraid of your own self.'

The young man thanked the witch-doctor and returned home. He noticed no change for the first few days. He did not go hunting with the young men of the tribe, but in himself they noticed nothing, for they thought he was ashamed.

One night, the young man felt a force driving him out of his hut. It was a dark night, the sort of night when no one dares to

169

go out of the village, but the young man felt neither fear nor apprehension, he only felt that his eyesight was at its sharpest and that his muscles were alive in his body. He had hardly crossed the threshold of his house, when not at all in horror, rather in joy, he realized that he had been transformed into a leopard. Silently he loped to the edge of the village and broke into a run over the grasslands. Before long he heard the footfalls of a herd of gazelles. He raced after them; he caught up with them, though they fled from him as if running from the wind. With one smooth spring he caught up with the leader of the herd. He pounced and although the gazelle fought for its life, it was soon overcome. And the young man, in the form of a leopard, dragged it back to his house.

But passion for the hunt did not die down in him. For a second time he raced out over the grasslands, and before long a second gazelle joined the first. Thus he hunted until the first light of dawn. Eventually he returned to the village, silent and unobserved and slipped into his house.

When he rose in the morning, he was a man again. He rose later than usual and he felt an unaccustomed fatigue. He only dimly remembered his nocturnal hunt, and so he was surprised by the loud cries of wonder which greeted him. Yes, he really had brought home the game which lay before the threshold of his house.

From that day forth, no one dared to mock him. Though no one saw him hunt, everyone saw the results which from time to time appeared in front of his house. Everyone came to admire him, because he was without doubt the most successful in the whole village and in the entire land.

He was begged by the young men of his tribe to take them hunting with him so that they might learn from him. But the young man remembered the words of the witch-doctor, and knowing that he hunted in his leopard form never consented to it.

His hunting fame grew and he became an eligible bridegroom. He sent his wooers to the father of the most beautiful girl in the land, and he was not refused.

The day came when he was to pay a visit to his bride. He dressed himself in his finest clothes, took many beautiful and costly gifts for his bride and for her bridesmaids and happily set out on his journey. He went joyfully, he wanted to run, and the basket which he carried seemed an unnecessary burden. He thought about his bride, this most beautiful girl, and he thought how desirable she was. In his heart he saw her throat and his legs burst into life; he threw aside the basket,

and set off at a run. He ran with long, light steps and
seemingly tireless, he ran all the way to the bend in the stream
where his bride and her attendants were bathing. From afar he
heard their happy cries, and he increased his speed. Then he
saw them. They were splashing in the shallow water,
swimming among the rocks and diving into the pools. Their
wet bodies shone and their white teeth flashed. And his bride
was the most beautiful of them all, her laughter the most
carefree.

Unnoticed he ran out on the river bank and was about to
call out to the girls when one of the girls caught sight of him
and screamed. He did not hear what she cried out, but he saw
that all the rest of the girls suddenly stood up in the water and
stared at him in horror. They began to cry in fear and then
they plunged headlong towards the opposite bank where in
panic they tried to scramble up on dry land. But he did not
wait. With swift jumps he ran a little way further upstream
where rocks formed a bridge across the river. There, he
jumped over the rocks and blocked the girls' path. They were
no longer screaming. Now each of them tried with all her

strength to escape from him. At last he found his bride. He saw how slender and beautiful she was as she fled towards her village. He set off at a run after her; he ran, his legs not touching the grass. He saw her in front of him, saw her smooth throat. Just one leap – and she would be his.

Suddenly he recoiled. He slowed his pace and looked at himself. And he saw that not he, but the leopard in him, was pursuing the girl. He realized that he did not want to make her his wife, but his prey, that he did not wish her to live at his side, but to lie dead beneath his feet.

But he could not stop himself. The prey fled before him, and he raced on after her. He felt how his whole body was preparing for the final spring.

'But I must not!' he cried out, but a terse leopard's roar issued from his throat. He saw his bride turn her head, he saw her terrified eyes, her slender hands. Then she stumbled, fell and terrified she waited for him to attack her.

'No I must not!' he wanted to shout again, and he concentrated all his will-power on holding back his leap. He saw blackness form before his eyes; he jumped, he thrust out his claws, and he did not feel her warm blood which flowed over his fingers.

Later when he came to his senses, he was again a man. He was weak and he could hardly stand. He looked for his bride, but she was gone. He was afraid to look in the direction where he sensed she had escaped. He turned, and with bowed head slowly retraced his steps. He did not know how he got to the other side of the river. He walked slowly towards his village. He came to the spot where he had thrown away his basket, and sadly he looked at the gifts he had bought with him. Finally he pulled himself together and arrived home as the sun was setting.

For some days he refused to go out. He did not answer his friends when they spoke to him. He became terrified of the dark. No, not of the dark, but of himself, of the desires and the powers that were within him.

After some days he recovered a little and his first thought was of the witch-doctor. Now he understood what he had wanted to tell him, now he knew what it was to be afraid of oneself!

He went to see him as soon as he was fit to travel. The old witch-doctor greeted him on his threshold, a gentle smile on his lips.

'I know, young man, what brings you here to me. I knew even then that you would discover that fear which is the most terrible of all human emotions. But I told you that there would be no help for you. I can do nothing for you,' he said.

'Surely there is some cure that will rid me of this curse, that I once thought was a blessing?' moaned the young man.

'There is only one remedy, but it is even more costly than the first. I do not know whether you are willing to pay such a high price.'

'I shall renounce my reputation as a great hunter, and I want to be the man I was before,' said the young man.

'You are offering a small price,' the witch-doctor smiled sadly, 'but you cannot even pay that. Look, you know very well that once a person gains a reputation, he cannot renounce it with words, whether it is good or bad. They stopped ridiculing you because they recognized you as a good hunter. And as a good hunter they will remember you long after you die.'

'Then what price must I pay?' asked the young man.

'Only with your life can you overcome the eternal fear that you will harm the ones you love,' said the witch-doctor.

'With my life?' the young man reflected.

'Those were my words,' said the witch-doctor.

'Very well,' said the young man. 'I shall pay that price. I would rather die at once than never in my life know when the wish might come over me to harm the people I love.'

Then the witch-doctor again gave him a brew of powerful herbs to drink and put him into a deep sleep in which he saw more than when wakeful and heard voices that the wakeful do not hear. And he chanted a spell over him and spoke the secret names of gods and spirits.

Then when the young man awoke from his sleep, the witch-doctor said to him:

'Return to your native village and live as you once lived before you became what you were until this moment. You will no longer be a hunter, but what you truly gained in that time, you will never lose. Your experience will remain with you, and out of it, the reputation of a wise man. You shall have to live like a just human being; that is the price which I asked of you and which you were willing to pay.'

And the young man returned home and never again did he long to become a great hunter. His reputation as a wise man spread and believing in him, people entrusted their property to him. He lived up to that trust and soon he became the owner of great herds, and he received his longed-for bride, who had now recovered from her wounds. Not as his prey did he receive her, but as his reward.

The Pagoda
of Thunder
Peak

The shores of the Lake of the West were alive with activity
on that spring day. The surface of the lake was criss-
crossed with the boats of fishermen and boatmen ferrying
travellers to the distant shore, where among the monasteries
and temples towered the Pagoda of Thunder Peak. It was the
fifth day of the fourth month, the Festival of Light and
Radiance. Gaily dressed people were burning fragrant candles
in the temples and monasteries in memory of their dead.

Young Su Hsien was among all those people. He was a
quiet youth, gentle and modest. He had been orphaned in the
dawn of his childhood and had grown up in the family of his
sister, who still took care of him, although he was employed
as an assistant in a pharmacy. That day he had requested some
free time at noon, so that he could honour the memory of his
dead parents. But he knew that this was the busiest day in the
pharmacy so he hurried on his return journey as soon as he
had lit a candle in the temple and heard the prayers of the
monks. He strode quickly to the lake and looked for a boat.
At last he saw a ferryman whom he knew and called out to
him. When the boat tied up and Su Hsien climbed aboard, a
strong wind rose, and the sky became overcast with heavy
black clouds which opened and a heavy downpour burst from
the sky. Su Hsien was pleased that he had caught the boat in
time.

Just as the boat put off from the shore, the ferryman saw
two young ladies without umbrellas standing on the shore.
The younger of the two waved desparately to the ferryman
asking him to take them too. Su Hsien agreed and with many
apologies and thanks, the young women took their places in
the boat.

Both of them were extraordinarily beautiful. The elder had

clear, shining eyes, a high white forehead, and black hair combed in a complicated, rather old-fashioned way. The younger one was dressed in gay colours and her hair was tied with red ribbons in the fashion of young girls. She was apparently a companion to her mistress.

Meanwhile, the rain grew heavier. It was as though there was nothing in the whole world but this open expanse of water, the rain and this little boat. Su Hsien and the young lady were silent, and looked at one another covertly now and then. Su Hsien had never met such a beautiful woman before, but he did not dare to speak to her. Then the younger girl herself began to talk, and gradually she learned not only his name, but also that he was an orphan and now worked in a pharmacy. She in turn told him that her mistress, Miss Pai Su-chen, had also become an orphan. She had lost her mother when she was very young. Her father had been a high official in the capital. Not long ago he had moved to the city of Hang-chou and retired there, but he had died and of all the family only Miss Pai and herself were left. Her name was Hsiao Ch'ing. They knew no one in Hang-chou, and they were hardly more than strangers there.

The time went by so quickly as they talked, that they were all surprised when the boat docked. The rain had not slackened, and both ladies were reluctant to step out into it. Su Hsien offered them his umbrella. After long hesitation they accepted the umbrella, and asked him to come and pick it up at their house near the Gate of Limpid Waves.

That day Su waited impatiently until the pharmacist finally gave him permission to close the shop. And Su hurried to the Gate of Limpid Waves. He could hardly remember when he had last been in that quarter, and he wondered how he might ask for directions to the home of the official, Mr Pai. He wandered helplessly, wondering on which gate to knock, when suddenly Hsiao Ch'ing peered out from one of the gates.

'Oh, so it is you, young man,' she greeted him gaily. 'I had a feeling that you might be coming. I hope you did not lose too much of your valuable time in looking for our house. Come in, the young mistress is expecting you.'

'I shall not detain you. I only came for my umbrella,' said Su Hsien politely refusing the invitation. But Hsiao Ch'ing persuaded him to accept. 'We live here so alone, we know no one in Hang-chou, and after all we have already become acquainted with you.'

Su Hsien was ushered into the reception room. Hsiao Ch'ing brought tea and cakes and than Miss Pai came and

thanked him once again for the kindness he had shown them. Slowly the conversation began to flow, as time passed Pai Su-chen and Su Hsien lost their shyness and spoke more freely. As they talked they found that they really liked each other. Then Su Hsien began to sigh quietly. He felt as though he had always known Pai Su-chen, yet at the same time he realized that he must leave – and as soon as he left, he would have no reason to return. The conversation began to dwindle, until at last Hsiao Ch'ing intervened:

'Dear young sir, you know that we live here in isolation and that we know no one in Hang-chou. We have no one to whom we could turn as an intermediary. Forgive me if I do not uphold all the rules of courtesy, but I think that under these circumstances, the intermediary can quite properly be me.'

Su Hsien stared at her in amazement and could not manage to utter a single word. Hsiao Ch'ing continued:

'The young lady is an orphan and you are without parents, so I can speak to you both directly. Miss Pai Su-chen has fallen in love with you, and I think that you feel the same.

Why not become engaged to be married?'

Su Hsien was stunned by this unexpected proposal. Pai Su-chen blushed with shame and tried to run from the room. But Hsiao Ch'ing caught her at once, preventing her. Su Hsien flushed in confusion, turned to Hsiao Ch'ing:

'I hardly dare to permit myself the thought that I could become the husband of your mistress. Why, I am just a poor orphan and I have nothing of my own. I live with my sister and the only income I have is as an assistant in a pharmacy.'

Hsiao Ch'ing replied that Pai Su-chen was not looking for a wealthy husband. From their short encounter, both had recognized Su Hsien's modesty, his honesty and his earnestness, and for that reason, she, Hsiao Ch'ing, wholeheartedly approved of the match. What is more they had enough money for the necessities of life and if Su Hsien agreed to the marriage they would have the security of his protection.

And so in the end, both young people decided that they would be married that very evening – for why should they delay when they had no parents to consult? So they drank the ceremonial goblet together, they bowed to one another, they honoured the memory of their parents, and Hsiao Ch'ing pronounced them husband and wife.

The next day, Su Hsien introduced Pai Su-chen to his sister and brother-in-law. His sister rejoiced that he had found such a beautiful wife. She had not hoped to find a wife for him – where was she to get the money for the bride's family? And she liked Pai Su-chen from their first meeting. Then they all conferred together on what the young couple should do next. Pai Su-chen suggested that Su Hsien establish his own pharmacy.

'As an assistant you have no doubt gained a great deal of knowledge, and I learned something about healing herbs from my father, for he studied the natural sciences for his own pleasure.'

The young couple found an abandoned house in a neighbourhood where there was no pharmacy, and they established themselves there and they called their shop 'The Hall that Harbours Peace'. Thanks to the industry of Su Hsien and the wisdom of Pai Su-chen, who could diagnose and relieve every illness, the pharmacy prospered. Soon they had to hire several assistants so that they could cope with all the work.

Su Hsien often gave thanks in his soul for the heavy rainstorm on the Lake of the West which had actually introduced him to his beloved Pai Su-chen. His happiness was

177

crowned when Pai informed him that she was expecting his child.

Neither Pai Su-chen nor Hsiao Ch'ing knew their way about Hang-chou and its surroundings, and so Su Hsien accompanied them on short trips into the beautiful countryside and to the distant parts of the town. Pai and Hsiao Ch'ing could never get their fill of the market-place. How they loved to stroll from shop to shop, gaily buying things they would never need. With great pleasure they listened to the tales of the professional storytellers or marvelled at the skill of the acrobats.

One day they all set off to a distant market-place where they joined the noisy throng and amused themselves happily. Suddenly the people began to draw back respectfully, until an old monk with a clean-shaven head appeared, striding down the road. His thin lips were closed tightly and his small piercing eyes were fastened directly in front of him. Suddenly he stopped, sank his gaze to Su Hsien, raised his forefinger and said in a loud voice:

'Unhappy man, I see that you are surrounded by a black aura. You are living in the midst of demons and your life is in danger!'

The noisy throng around them fell silent in horror, Su Hsien whitened and protested:

'Honourable monk, what sort of nonsense are you saying? I live here with only my wife and her maid. How could there be demons here?'

The monk snapped:

'Then they are probably the demons. I am telling you what I see.'

The people surrounding them stepped back and began to examine Pai Su-chen and Hsiao Ch'ing suspiciously. For the monk was the renowned Fa-hai from the monastery on Golden Mountain, famous throughout the land as an implacable enemy and subduer of all spirits and demons.

Su Hsien was horrified and did not know what to do. He was horrified at the thought that his beloved wife was a demon. He remembered that he knew nothing about her family except what his wife and Hsiao Ch'ing had told him.

It seemed that the screaming crowd would turn on Pai Su-chen and Hsiao Ch'ing. Fa-hai stood motionless, smiling contemptuously. Suddenly Pai Su-chen took several paces forward and stared intently into the eyes of the monk. To the astonishment of all the spectators, Fa-hai suddenly floated silently into the air, at a height of several feet, and as long as

Pai Su-chen stared at him, he remained suspended there, powerless. After a moment Pai Su-chen calmly turned around, Fa-hai fell to the ground and strode away in a rage.

'Look at me, I am an ordinary person like all of you. My body casts a shadow and my clothes have seams. My father studied magic, and because I was his only child, he instructed me in the art. What that monk can do, I can do too.'

The crowd calmed down, and after much discussion, they went about their business.

Su Hsien was astonished. Before he had time to recover from Fa-hai's accusation, he was startled by the unexpected knowledge of his own wife. But he allowed himself to be convinced by Pai Su-chen's explanation and they all returned home together.

He would have been even more astonished had he known the truth about Pai Su-chen and Hsiao Ch'ing.

Far from Hang-chou towers the mountain range of O-mei. Its mountain peaks and deep valleys nestling in the clouds were a haven for all those who tried to discover the mysteries of nature and comprehend the meaning of their lives. Famous monasteries were built on the mountain slopes, and those who ventured to the highest were rewarded by a look at Buddha's face mirrored in the clouds above the dark valleys. Immortals lived among the mountain peaks and holy men lived in the valleys. The beauty of nature and the perfection of those beings, both mortal and immortal who lived there, filled the mountain range with serenity.

In a dark cave near the mountain peaks, a white snake resolved to follow the way of Buddha. It renounced all violence and the endangering of the lives of other beings. After a full thousand years of earnest meditation, it succeeded in gaining mastery over its body and character and so it came close to the understanding of all things. Finally it attained such a level of knowledge that it acquired human form.

In its new likeness as a beautiful young woman, it eagerly sought out wise teachers so that it could further deepen its knowledge and understanding. On one such journey, she met a young girl who had achieved human form in the same way through painstaking meditation and practice. Originally she had been a snake of a dark green colour, and she had set out on the road to perfection several hundred years before. The two girls made a compact of sisterhood and friendship. The white snake took on the name Pai Su-chen, which means Clear White Truth, and the green snake began to call itself Hsiao Ch'ing, or Little Green One. From that time on they were always together and they supported one another in their endeavours. Gradually they became more and more curious about the human world. Their teachers had left the world of human cares behind but they had not forgotten it and often mentioned it in their discussions. The two young women began to long to know more of it.

And so one day Pai Su-chen and Hsiao Ch'ing went away from their mountain home, and set off to the town of Hang-chou. Enchanted by the exquisite beauty of nature, the loftiness of the buildings and the tumultuous life of human beings, they were strolling along the shores of the Lake of the West, when they caught sight of Su Hsien and love captured the heart of Pai Su-chen. She decided that she would not go back to the cool mountains, but would try living a life among people, with all its joys and sorrows. Hsiao Ch'ing did not want to leave her, and so they selected roles for themselves as a lady and her maid. And because they did not know how they could begin to talk to Su Hsien, Pai Su-chen called up that sudden rain which led her all the way to that encounter in the market-place.

It seemed that everything was the same in the small household after the incident in the market-place. Su Hsien suffered doubts, but he was convinced of the truth of Pai Su-chen's love for him. Why every one of her actions contradicted the evil words of Fa-hai! For she helped people and brought them comfort and relief!

However, when the enraged Fa-hai returned from the market-place to his monastery on Golden Mountain, he concentrated all his skills on discovering who Pai Su-chen and Hsiao Ch'ing were. He learned of their origins and the fact that they had set out on the road to righteousness hundreds of years before. He also learned that Pai's feeling for Su Hsien was true and deep and that she had already done many beneficial things for people. Perhaps he could have contented himself with that knowledge and left Su Hsien and his household in peace. But Fa-hai did not consider the matter in this light. He had discovered that Pai Su-chen and Hsiao Ch'ing were not ordinary people, and he resolved to force them to return to the mountains. After all, he was upholding the law. He would show everyone his power and strength, and would punish Pai Su-chen for making him lose face in front of so many people!

Fa-hai did not delay but descended the mountain and went directly to the 'Hall that Harbours Peace' and asked the assistants to call Su Hsien to him.

Su Hsien was very uneasy when they announced the monk Fa-hai to him. He remembered what had happened in the market-place, and he would have preferred to avoid the monk, but he did not know how. So he greeted him and asked him what he wished.

Fa-hai had a very grave expression on his face:

'I do not wish anything. I have come in your interest so that I might convince you that you are in deadly danger. Your wife and her companion are demons. Believe in my words and beware.'

Su Hsien grew deathly pale, but he decided not to be influenced by the monk's words. Fa-hai did not insist but continued in a calm voice:

'I knew that you would not believe me at once, because you are completely in the power of unclean forces. But you will be persuaded that I am right. If you obey me, it will not be too late for your salvation. Soon the Festival of the Double Fives will take place. On that day give your wife some strong yellow wine to drink, and you will see her true form.'

The fifth day of the fifth month drew near, the Festival of the Double Fives, when the height of the summer was celebrated. The doors to the pharmacy were never still. Instead of buying medicines, people came to buy fragrant herbs and candles, or they brought eggrolls made of bamboo shoots and fruit as tokens of their gratitude to Pai Su-chen for her help during their sickness. In all the bustle, Pai Su-chen did not remember until the day before the holiday, that according to the laws of nature, at noon on the festival of the height of the summer, every living being reveals its own true image. Pai Su-chen was glad that she had one thousand years of strict training behind her. She trusted that she would succeed in retaining her human form through the fateful noontime. But what about Hsiao Ch'ing, who had much less experience? She advised her to lock herself in her room and say that she was ill. As for herself, there was nothing for her but to trust in her own power. If she tried to hide somewhere, she would only arouse Su Hsien's doubts anew.

The fifth day of the fifth month dawned. Hsiao Ch'ing had shut herself up in her room in the morning, feigning a sudden illness, and Pai Su-chen tended her. She spent as much time as possible in her own room for it was dreadfully hot and she was exhausted.

Noon drew near. Su Hsien closed the shop and let the assistants go, so that they might be in time to see the ride of the dragon boats on the lake. He was looking forward to

spending time with Pai Su-chen and going to the festival with
her. But Pai Su-chen excused herself saying that she was
feeling terribly tired because of the heat. She told Su Hsien to
go by himself. She would certainly be feeling better in a little
while, and then they would go again together.

Su Hsien was annoyed. Hsiao Ch'ing's sudden illness and
now Pai Su-chen's nausea aroused his suspicion. He
remembered the advice of Fa-hai. He tried pushing the
thought aside. Why, there was nothing unusual in the fact that
a woman who was expecting a child should feel nausea in such
heat. So he sat and deliberated whether he should urge Pai
Su-chen to drink some of the wine prepared for the festival.
Finally he made up his mind.

'These are all nothing but foolish thoughts. If that monk is
right, then I shall see what sort of situation I am in, and if he is
not right, a little wine will not hurt Pai Su-chen.'

Su Hsien took the bottle of wine and glasses, and
comforted, went to Pai Su-chen. Pai Su-chen was still resting
on her bed, and it was evident that she was feeling unwell. Su
Hsien came in with a full glass and urged her to drink it. Pai
Su-chen did not dare refuse. She felt that she would only
awake Su Hsien's suspicions if she did so, and with
determination she drank the glass of strong yellow wine. She
felt a great lassitude come over her and she asked Su Hsien to
leave her alone for a while, so that she could sleep a little and

recover. Su Hsien felt sorry for her and did not know how to help her. It would probably be best, he thought, if he let her sleep.

So he sat alone downstairs in the shop with the last of the wine. He was worried about Pai Su-chen and he listened carefully so that he would hear her when she got up. Absolute silence reigned upstairs. It seemed strange and so he decided that he would go and find out how Pai Su-chen was feeling. Carefully he tiptoed up the stairs so that he would not wake her and quietly opened the door of the room where she was sleeping.

Then he screamed in horror and fell to the ground. On the bed in the darkened room glowed the coiled white body of an enormous snake!

All was quiet. The sun sank lower, and the town returned to normal after the festival. Towards evening Hsiao Ch'ing woke up and went to look at Pai Su-chen. What a shock she had when she saw the dead Su Hsien lying by the door, and on the bed, Pai Su-chen in a deep sleep!

Quickly she woke her up and told her what had happened. Pai Su-chen began to cry as though her heart were broken and between her sobs, she told Hsiao Ch'ing how Su Hsien had brought the yellow wine and she had drunk it. Then she had felt such a faintness that she had fallen asleep. And at noon her true image had revealed itself, probably at the moment when Su Hsien had entered the room. Pai Su-chen felt that she had killed Su Hsien. The monk had been right when he had warned her husband of her. What good had her great love been! Pai Su-chen would not be comforted. They lifted Su Hsien onto the bed, and in tears they pondered on what they could do to help him. Pai Su-chen tried to remember all that she had learned of healing from the wise men in the mountains. She tended Su Hsien through the night, until, at last, towards morning his blood began to flow again and gradually he began to breathe.

In the morning Su Hsien awoke with a dreadful headache. He tried to remember what had happened, and suddenly a huge white snake appeared before his eyes, coiled up on the bed! There, where his wife had been lying! In his horror, Su Hsien's heart shuddered again and the blood drained from his face. He remembered Fa-hai's warning and his advice about the wine. He was certain now that he was in the power of strange forces. Su Hsien tossed and turned on the bed, and memories of his first meeting with Pai Su-chen raced through his head. Now everything seemed suspicious and his worst fears were realized. But as these thoughts flashed through his mind, Pai Su-chen's kind and beautiful face appeared before him. He remembered everything she had done for him within the short time of their marriage by her gentleness. And Pai Su-chen was expecting his child, which both of them had been looking forward to with such joy! But that thought was promptly chased away by the picture of a white snake coiled up on her bed.

Tortured by cruel doubts, Su Hsien stayed in bed all afternoon.

Several days passed. Su Hsien tortured himself by thinking about what he should do. He was afraid of Pai Su-chen and Hsiao Ch'ing, so he spent all his days and nights in the shop. At the same time he tried to convince himself of the possibility that he had had too much wine to drink on that fateful day and had imagined it all. Pai Su-chen understood what was going on in his heart, but she did not know how to comfort him. Su Hsien rebuffed her, and seemed to mistrust her more.

Su Hsien's torment grew greater and greater. At last he made up his mind that he would go and see Fa-hai and ask him for his advice. He wanted to tell him about what he had seen during the festival, and of Pai Su-chen's nature; how kind she was to people and to him. Perhaps the wise monk would advise him on his best course of action.

Without saying a word to anyone at home, he set off one day to visit the monastery on Golden Mountain. As soon as he had announced his name at the gate, he was instantly led to Fa-hai.

'I have been expecting you. At last your eyes have been opened! You are in the power of the spirits of the mountain of O-mei, the white and the green snakes. You must give me your whole-hearted assistance. Unless you wish to fall into deadly danger again, you must never again go back down among people. You will remain here under my protection and Buddha's. If you devote yourself to prayer earnestly like a monk, your life will be safe. Down there amongst people you would be delivered to the mercy of demons.'

Before Su Hsien could explain that he had only come to ask him for his advice, Fa-hai summoned several monks and ordered Su Hsien to be led away to a solitary cell.

'This man is in the power of unclean forces and he will only be saved by severe fasting and utter seclusion from people. Do not allow anyone to see him, or I shall punish you all severely.'

And so the unhappy Su Hsien, instead of receiving the

advice of a merciful monk, spent his long days locked in a lonely cell. Over and over again he contemplated his life with Pai Su-chen. He remembered her beauty, her goodness and her gentleness. His memories of her grew clearer and clearer, while the horror which he had experienced when he saw the white snake on her bed slowly began to fade.

Meanwhile, the peace of 'Hall that Harbours Peace', had been shattered. When Su Hsien had been at home and had avoided her, Pai Su-chen had understood his state of mind. She had hoped that her love would overcome his fear. When Su Hsien had disappeared without a word of farewell, however, Pai Su-chen realized the depth of the rift between them. She knew that Su Hsien had gone to see Fa-hai, to ask him for his help. Hsiao Ch'ing began to tell Pai Su-chen to leave her weak and ungrateful husband. They would return together to the mountain of O-mei, where everything had been so simple.

Pai Su-chen protested that it was not as easy as that:

'I bound myself to the human world with a firm bond. My love for Su Hsien is deep and true. And before long I shall bear his child. My own imperfection was the cause of my taking on my previous image after all and frightening him to death. Su Hsien, like so many humans, is afraid of the unknown, and surely we must understand that.'

And so Hsiao Ch'ing agreed with Pai Su-chen's decision to try to free Su Hsien from the power of the proud monk.

They told everyone that Su Hsien had gone away on a long journey, and they were closing the pharmacy for the time being. They paid the assistants, locked the house and set off to the monastery on Golden Mountain.

At the gates of the monastery, Pai Su-chen requested that

they kindly usher them to the famous Fa-hai. The monks announced them and shortly Pai Su-chen and Hsiao Ch'ing were stepping into the great hall of the monastery. At its centre sat the scowling Fa-hai, and as soon as he caught sight of them he shouted:

'You are insolent wretches! After everything that has happened you still dare to stain my monastery with your presence?'

But Pai Su-chen paid no attention and humbly stepped before Fa-hai.

'Illustrious master, I am aware that you know well who I am. I apologize profusely for my imprudent behaviour that day at the market-place. I am appealing to your kindness and I plead for mercy. Do not destroy the love that binds me to Su Hsien; allow him to go down amongst people.'

The humble words of Pai Su-chen angered Fa-hai even more. Nor did her assurances that she had neither harmed Su Hsien nor any other living being help her. The monk turned his face from her and declared:

'Spirits belong among spirits, demons among demons. They have no business to appear among humans. It makes no difference that you love your husband. I shall never consent to what is not right and proper.'

When he finished speaking, he raised his powerful staff into the air. He used it to overcome and subjugate spirits. Pai Su-chen realized that she would not persuade Fa-hai, and so she rose to the challenge of battle. Both girls unsheathed their magic swords and in the large hall a ferocious battle was unleashed. Fa-hai was indeed a powerful monk and had mastered many spells. Pai Su-chen and Hsiao Ch'ing were just on the point of succumbing to his power when Pai Su-chen called on the help of her companions in the water realm. At that instant the waves of the river at the foot of the mountains swelled. The water thundered towards the monastery gates in a mighty rush and flooded the whole region. The terrified monks fled. The water surged into the large hall where Pai Su-chen and Hsiao Ch'ing were battling. Snakes, turtles and fish, crabs and octopuses rushed in its wake. A new battle was unleashed, for Fa-hai called on the help of spirits who were in his power. For a long time the battle raged on, but then suddenly Pai Su-chen groaned out in pain. Hsiao Ch'ing leapt to her side in concern. Pai gestured to her helpers for them to return to their watery realm. She was not wounded, but weakened by her pregnancy, and could no longer continue the battle.

In a twinkling the waters subsided and silence settled on the monastery. Pai Su-chen and Hsiao Ch'ing walked sadly away. Fa-hai allowed them to go. He felt that he had to perfect his skills further, so that he might defeat Pai Su-chen. Then some monks brought him the news that Su Hsien had vanished during the battle. Fa-hai shrugged off the news. Let him go where he wishes, for Fa-hai would get his way in the end!

Dusk was drawing nigh as Pai Su-chen and Hsiao Ch'ing walked slowly towards the Lake of the West. They walked all the way to the famous Broken Bridge over the dam to the Lake of the West. Its lofty arch was lost in the evening twilight. In exhaustion, Pai Su-chen sat down on the balustrade. At that moment a man appeared walking towards the bridge from the other side. Pai was already prepared to stand up and walk on, when she realized that the man was Su Hsien! Both of them cried out and for a while neither could speak. Their joy at finding one another was mingled with the pain of betrayal.

Su Hsien wept with emotion and begged Pai Su-chen to forgive him for all the suffering they had been through.

'I know that you are not ordinary humans, but I am no longer afraid of you. I have recognized the fidelity of Pai Su-chen and I promise that I shall never leave her again under any circumstances. I know now that both of you have finer hearts than the pitiless Fa-hai.'

The couple considered where they would go. They did not want to go back just yet to their home in the 'Hall That Harbours Peace'. Fa-hai would most certainly find them there again at the first opportunity. So they agreed that they would go to Su Hsien's sister. In peace and contentment they lived there for several months. Pai Su-chen gave birth to a healthy boy and it seemed to everyone that their happiness was complete.

Then one day, Su Hsien's sister called to him:

'Brother, you have a visitor. An old monk!'

Su Hsien turned pale and at once went to warn Pai Su-chen and Hsiao Ch'ing:

'Alas, alas, that old Fa-hai is here again! How can we escape from him?'

'You shall not escape from me,' came a cold and unfriendly voice from behind him.

Fa-hai stepped into the room. In his hands he held a red metal bowl, the sort that monks use when they beg for alms. He held it stretched out in front of him, and in a thunderous voice, he called out:

'White snake, reveal your true image! Your hour has struck!'

At that instant Pai Su-chen let out a painful sigh and was transformed into a white snake. Fa-hai turned his shining red metal bowl over on the white snake. The magic bowl engulfed the whole snake within itself. Without a word, Fa-hai lifted it up and walked away. With the red bowl in his outstretched hands, he strode all the way to the Pagoda of Thunder Peak. He hid the bowl with the snake under it and commanded the pagoda to never again allow the white snake out amongst people. He was not moved by Su Hsien's tears, nor his tiny son, nor by the pleas of his sister, but haughtily returned to his monastery on Golden Mountain.

At first Hsiao Ch'ing wavered, wondering whether she should not stay with Pai Su-chen's son, but then she made up her mind.

'Su Hsien's sister will take good care of the boy. I shall return to the mountains and I promise you that I shall do everything I can to gain the knowledge that will enable me to free Pai Su-chen from her captivity. Wait for me, I shall surely return one day.'

And so Su Hsien was left alone with his son. For many years they went together every day to the Pagoda of Thunder Peak. The gentle and good Pai Su-chen abided in his memory and he waited for Hsiao Ch'ing to come and set her free.

The Lioness

'He is a lion, he is a lion,' sang the warriors of the tribe. 'He is a lion and trees topple 'neath the blows of his paws. He is a lion and the grass bursts into flame at his breath. He is a lion and there is no one to match him.'

But women were lionesses too. Legends are told of their deeds, and songs are sung.

In one village there lived a young man who was strong and brave, but he was an orphan, so poor that he could buy neither butter nor oil. He had reached the age of manhood long ago, but there was no wife in his hut, for who would give his daughter to a poor man?

'How will he feed his wife? What will he give his children when they cry with hunger?' asked the fathers of the village maidens. And he, when he saw that he would have no success in his own village, took up his basket and went to follow the sun.

As he lay at night on his first camping-ground, he saw a lion following his tracks. He saw a lion, how he sniffed his meagre belongings; he saw a lion, how he circled the place where he lay, and he felt he would not live to see the morning. But the lion vanished in the undergrowth and left only the crushed grass behind him.

'Perhaps the lion is not hungry,' he said to himself. 'Perhaps the lion does not consider me worth devouring. Neither people nor lions care for poor men,' he said to himself.

Then the sun lit up the world, and a man in good health rejoices to be alive. Perhaps somewhere there is a bowl of meat waiting, who knows? Perhaps somewhere a wife awaited and a family of healthy children.

But the world is large and night came before the end of the

journey. And the lion came again and circled the place where that man lay down to sleep. He could feel the lion's breath upon him when the lion spoke in a husky voice:

'I know your thoughts and they are better than your flesh. I did not come to devour you; I wish to give you my daughter as your wife. I have enough food, all the bush is my hunting-ground. I care nothing for herds and riches, nor does my daughter need them. She wants a good man who will care for her and bring up her children well. I see into your mind and I know that you are the best husband for my daughter. Sleep now in contentment, for tomorrow I shall bring her to you.'

A poor man cannot choose and an unarmed man cannot defend himself. Perhaps that woman will not know how to cook, perhaps her children will be lion cubs and will maul their own father to death. But better to live to see the morning! Better a lioness for a wife than no wife at all, better a lioness for a wife than loneliness and exile.

The lion circled the spot once more and disappeared again into the darkness.

A poor man does not sleep well; all sorts of thoughts whirl in his head, and as he falls asleep, dreams frighten him. But in the morning, he awoke to find a beautiful woman by his side, gazing out of shining eyes and smiling with beautiful white teeth.

'I do not know who you are, young woman, I do not know what you want here. You are beautiful, but all the same I must send you away. It is morning, and at any moment my father-in-law the lion will come with my lioness wife.'

'I am your lioness wife,' the girl laughed, 'I am that bride who was promised you.'

'You are a lioness, beautiful girl? Your arms are strong but they are not a lion's paws. Your legs are sturdy but they are not a lion's paws. And your breath is fragrant; how can you be a lioness?'

'You will see whether I am a lioness or not,' the girl declared. Just be a good husband to me, and I shall be a good wife to you.'

Why wander through strange country when you have a beautiful wife? Why think about poverty as the sun is rising? Instead they returned to the poor man's village.

'Look, that young man is bringing a wife,' declared the women of the tribe.

'Look, he is bringing a beautiful woman,' declared the men of the tribe.

'He is bringing a beautiful wife into his wretched hut, and he does not even have a garden to till,' declared the chieftain of the tribe and he gave him a piece of fallow land.

Where there is land, there is also well-being. And where there is a woman, warmth rises from the hearth. And the children of that woman were well-fed and healthy. They were like all other children, only stronger, perhaps they grew more quickly and they were soon able to help their father.

'She is a good woman,' the villagers decided.

'It is she who brought us good fortune,' said the villagers.

'Our village grows wealthy and we prosper. And all this has happened since she came to live with us.'

But when life is good, greed raises its head.

'We could have it all, we need only have manly hearts.'

'We could take it all, we need only have sharp spears!' said the men of the neighbouring tribe.

They strode out to the sound of drums, their steps accompanied by the music of flutes.

Through the night they walked the narrow trail, then at dawn they attacked.

Three days and nights the battle raged, four days without result. At sunset of the fourth day it seemed that the villagers would not hold off the attacks of their enemy. And then, when the enemy withdrew to spend the night around their fires, the lioness woman went out and stalked their tracks.

Just one lone guard was vigilant, while the rest slept. Just one lone guard was vigilant, and circled the fires. And on lion's paws the lioness woman slipped silently through the bushes, with a lion's spring she knocked down the guard and with lion's teeth she broke his neck. Then she went among the fires and to the right and to the left she sowed destruction. Under her paw, spines cracked, under her teeth skulls shattered. She walked among the fires, and left behind her tracks drenched with the enemy's blood. Those who did not awake in time, never woke again. And those who did awake in time, fled into the darkness, sobbing with fear.

The lioness stalked among the fires, but she did not leave their circle unharmed. Only one man was prepared, only one was watchful, and he recalled his old wounds. His old wounds which he had sustained in battles long ago. He stood up, weighed his spear and hurled it at the lioness. The spear pierced the darkness and sank into her hip. Then thunder crashed and wind rose up in the trees.

With her last remaining strength, the lioness ran back among the fires. With her last remaining strength she crept

between the bushes, and on her belly, with the spear pierced into her right side, she dragged herself to her husband's hut. There she lay on the mat, her body half lioness, half woman.

The enemy were overwhelmed, for though it is possible to stand against spears, and though it is possible to withstand the blows of clubs, it is impossible to withstand lion's hungering for human flesh.

So the enemy withdrew and abandoned their attack on their more prosperous neighbours. They withdrew, and all that remained of their camp were the burned out fires and the cries of orphaned children.

All the women of the village went out for water, all ground millet in front of their husband's huts, only the lioness woman scratched at her wound with her weakened paw. And her sons walked helplessly around her, not knowing how to help her. And on the fourth day, the husband left and went to see the witch-doctor.

'My wife is a lioness,' he said to the witch-doctor, 'as a lioness she was wounded by a spear in her side and now she cannot rise from her bed and she will die. She is a good woman and she brought my sons up well. See to it that she does not die.'

'If your wife is a lioness and if she was wounded as a lioness, then her life is escaping through her lioness veins. She does not have enough strength to live on as a lioness, but she certainly has enough strength to live on as a woman,' said the witch-doctor; and he lit four fires and beat on a wooden drum.

'Within four fires I hold a woman,
The good woman of a brave man.
Within four fires I hold a woman,
With the drum I set the lioness free',
chanted the witch-doctor.

And the spirits of life waged war in that woman with the spirits of death, and the spirits of death were defeated. Four fires saved the soul of the woman, and the soul of the lioness departed, accompanied by the beating of a drum.

'She is a lioness, she is a lioness,' sang the warriors of the tribe. 'She is a lioness and trees crack under the blow of her paws. She is a lioness and the dry grass blazes at her breath. She is a lioness and never was there one like her; and never will be again.'

But she was not a lioness, she was a woman and the smell of cooking rose from her hearth. But her sons grew quickly, they were hard-working and fruitful. And never again did that tribe know hunger.

Seketoa

Preacher Siaosi, who was a descendant of an old chieftain's family and enjoyed universal esteem on the islands, asked the old Maatu one evening to take him tuna fishing to the deep waters near the volcanic island of Tafahi. Maatu was not very enthusiastic, because he did not think that Siaosi could handle a rod and line, and he was definitely not a proficient rower. When he glanced at the sky, he was satisfied that the next day would be fine, and he waved his hand and told Siaosi to join them the following day. He would not have invited the preacher if a strong wind threatened to rise or if they were planning to sail into distant waters. As it was going to be a fine day there was no harm in giving Siaosi the pleasure of a day at sea again.

The next day, when Maatu and his nephew were preparing the boat, his own wife asked him if she might come out with him. In the old days, the fishermen never took their wives out to sea with them because they would have disobeyed an important taboo, and the expedition could have been put into danger. However, Maatu finally agreed to allow his wife to join them. Why should he let himself be influenced by the old superstitions, when the preacher would safeguard them against all evil spirits?

The sea sparkled like a huge blue mirror and there was not a cloud in the sky. Except above Tafahi island where a motionless puff of white cloud hung above the mountain peak, but no danger threatened from that quarter. The boat sailed swiftly, and before the sun rose above their heads, they were at their destination. The hunt was successful; they hauled in one tuna after another and before long they had caught enough.

On the return trip, Maatu and his nephew sang an old

ballad about Seketoa, who fought for his people all his life, and when he fell, fatally wounded on his left side, he was changed into a fish.

'Seketoa, plunging into the waves,
cried: I shall be faithful to my people!'
sang Maatu.

'Seketoa, transformed into a fish,
guards fishermen and brings them help!'

When Maatu had finished singing, preacher Siaosi asked:

'So we are indebted to Seketoa for today's catch?'

Maatu said nothing, but it was clear that he did not like this remark.

'Why does he not show himself,' Siaosi asked. 'Why we could thank him properly then.'

Then Maatu said:

'Be quiet, preacher, and do not mock things that you do not understand.'

'Surely you do not believe in these tales?' laughed the preacher. 'Or perhaps you have seen Seketoa yourself?'

'My uncle's uncle saw him,' said Maatu's wife. 'He appeared to him in the likeness of a fish and guided him out of a storm.'

'Your uncle's uncle was a foolish man,' Siaosi cut her short.

'He believed in the old religion, but he was not foolish. He could call Seketoa forth.'

'This is no more than talk which will not stand up before the truth that I bring you,' said the preacher.

'If you say so, preacher, then it is certainly true,' said Maatu respectfully. 'I am probably a foolish man, but even I can call Seketoa forth.'

'Then why do you not call him forth?' asked the preacher.

'I am afraid,' said Maatu, 'but if you wish, I shall try to do so.'

And he leaned over the water and said quite softly, as though he rather wished that the mighty spirit would not hear him.

'If you are here, Seketoa, reveal yourself. Not because of me, but because of the preacher. And should you reveal yourself, do us no harm.'

For a while nothing happened. The preacher burst out laughing:

'You see. How could a figment of the imagination reveal itself when there is no substance to the story.'

And just then a small fish *matakelekele* appeared in front of the boat and they could see a healed-up white scar on its left

side. They were all frightened, but Siaosi laughed and said:

'I thought that Seketoa would choose to reveal himself in some more dignified form, at the moment he is very small fry.'

The water churned and when it had cleared again a small shark appeared.

'Look, a shark has devoured your Seketoa,' laughed the preacher, but he broke off at once, because he noticed that the shark had a small scar on his left side. But then he said:

'Why have you never seen a wounded shark?'

Suddenly the shark began to swim around the boat in a wide circle, and when he appeared in front of the boat, he was bigger than an adult man. And he continued to swim around them in wider and wider circles, until he had turned into the biggest blue shark that had ever been seen in those waters.

The preacher, murmuring prayers, tried to ward the shark away. But the shark only opened his jaws a little as if in silent laughter and turned towards the boat. In sudden terror the preacher seized the rifle which he had with him, and fired at the mighty head of the shark. The shark lashed his tail and dived under the boat.

At once the white puffs of clouds above the island of Tafahi grew threatening, and a fierce wind began to whip up the waves. In a moment the calm surface of the sea was furrowed with enormous waves, the boat began to toss about, and they had to throw all the fish they had caught overboard, as well as the preacher's gun, in order to lighten the boat and keep it above water. They could not possibly continue their journey home to the island of Niua Toputapu, and they had to look for a closer shelter. They saw a calm lagoon behind the coral reefs around the island of Tafahi. The waves were growing mightier all the time, and the sailors had a hard time finding

the entrance to the lagoon among the mountainous waves. When they finally reached it, the waves swept the boat into the narrows between the sharp coral reefs and instantly surged back, so that the boat ran aground on the shoal. Maatu and his nephew jumped out onto the narrow reef, and hardly had they helped Maatu's wife and the preacher onto the firm rocks when a new wave hurled the boat into the lagoon and carried it far away.

So they stood, clinging to one another, in utter helplessness. And an enormous shark circled in the water, so huge that it was greater than the largest galleon, and whenever it turned its side towards them, they could see the white scar over its healed wound.

Then the preacher who was expecting to be swept by the next wave into the jaws of that gigantic fish, screamed out, overcome with terror:

'What do you want of me, Seketoa? Are you a good spirit or a sea demon? How can I atone for my actions?'

At these words, the fish streaked towards the reef and it seemed that it meant to swallow them all at once. But when it was almost upon them, its teeth suddenly flashed as if in a disdainful smile, and it swerved to one side and vanished among the waves.

Before long the wind died down, the sky cleared and their boat drifted within their reach over the calm surface of the lagoon.

An Injustice
Exposed

The provincial officials Yeh Nin-fei and Wang Lieh were good friends and they spent many pleasant hours together. Both were honest men, and they terrified those corrupt officials with whom they came into contact on their official duties.

Recently, the two friends had seen each other only rarely, for their business affairs had taken them into various parts of the province. Then Yeh Nin-fei received news of the death of Wang Lieh. His family had the coffin and his remains transferred to his native village, where they buried him. Yeh Nin-fei was deeply grieved at the loss of his friend, and decided that he would go to Wang Lieh's grave to honour his memory as soon as the opportunity arose.

About three months went by after the death of Wang Lieh, and Yeh Nin-fei was sent on an inspection tour to the distant town of Hua-hsi. There had been many complaints against the governor and it was the very town where illness and death had overtaken Wang Lieh.

After a tiring journey, Yeh Nin-fei arrived in the town, settled in the local inn and carefully began to study documents and papers, which were in great disorder. The town governor had no compunction in accepting bribes, and the whole district had suffered from his neglect and malpractice. His own house, however, abounded in wealth and splendour, greater even than the dreams of mortal men.

One evening Yeh was sitting in his room absorbed in the documents, when the door quietly opened and a light waft of cool air blew into the room, causing the flame of the little lamp to quiver. Yeh Nin-fei looked up in surprise, but the door closed again and no one entered the room. It was probably a draught, Yeh Nin-fei thought to himself, and again buried himself in his work. But before he could find his place among the papers, he saw that his friend Wang Lieh sat on the other side of the table. He was sitting quietly and smiling gently. Yeh greeted him joyfully, but he was puzzled at his presence there.

'I did not even realize that you died here in this town. But why are you not yet home? I heard that your family had already had you transferred and performed the burial ceremonies. What are you doing delaying in this strange town? Surely, even as a ghost, you should already be home?'

'You are right,' Wang agreed with him. 'Except that such unpleasantness occurred, I hardly know how to tell you about it. I was kept here and in the meantime they took my body away. And now I am stranded here and I am unable to return home. I was left entirely penniless, and I do not have enough to pay the toll to all those underworld guards at the district borders. And you know yourself how far I must journey. When I learned that you had come into this town, I rejoiced. You are my only hope. I do not like to inconvenience you, but I have no other way of solving this situation. I must ask you for your kind financial assistance.'

Yeh gladly promised Wang that he would help him. It is after all a matter of course which friends need not even mention. He only asked approximately how much he would need, and promised that he would arrange everything the following day. Then he placed the documents into the coffer, and continued to question his friend:

'I do not wish to be intrusive, but could you tell me what actually happened to you.'

Wang waved his hand. 'It is such a long and complicated story, in the beginning I could hardly make head or tail of it myself. I should not like to deprive you of your valuable time, I see that you have a great deal of work.'

But Yeh Nin-fei urged his friend to tell him everything that he could. For when would they have another chance to talk together. And so after a moment Wang began to tell his story.

It was confused at first. As you know, I was sent here to Hua-si on an inspection tour. Before I could even begin, though, I fell ill. I had a very high fever and I died, without actually being aware of it. I was lying in the bed at the inn and suddenly the door opened forcefully and two guards rushed into the room. I just had time to think that they were in a fine state of affairs here, if guards could come bursting into the room of an official for no reason, but by then the guards had stepped right up to my bed. They looked dreadful. They were

all dressed in black, their waists were almost pinched in half by wide belts, they had ghastly pale, ominous faces and protruding red eyes. On their heads they had some strange sort of headdress with ornaments of black iron. Both held heavy chains in their hands. They tore me from my bed, tied my hands and brutally dragged me away.

On the way they did not speak one word, and in response to my questions they only jerked at my bonds. I did not even know how it was that I suddenly found myself in a spacious hall, surrounded all around by similar-looking guards. At the front behind a judge's bench sat an enormous judge. He had a green face in which huge piercing eyes shone beneath mighty black brows. Over his whole body there fell a thick red beard, through which he had thrust his arms and leaned on the desk. He looked at me with a stern stare, and icy shudders ran over my whole body.

The guards knocked me to my knees and stood at my side. The judge called me to state my name, and ordered a clerk, apparently a scribe, who was standing at a counter in front of

205

the judge's bench, to find my case in the book of accusations and punishments. I realized that I was standing before the underworld judge.

The scribe turned the leaves of a large book for a little while and then began to read in a monotonous voice:

'Wang, the official, is charged with the following: in addition to many offences which he committed against morality and honour with his profligate life and his corruption, many years ago he was the cause of the death of Chu Cheng. The said Chu Cheng after his death, filed an accusation with our court, which has been verified as truthful.'

I do not know how to describe to you how I felt at that moment. I was accused of an immoral life and corruption! And I knew no Chu Cheng, how then could I have caused his death? I was perspiring with anxiety and indignation, and fear sent chilly shudders up and down my back.

For the whole duration of the reading, the dreadful judge did not take his eyes from me, and when the scribe fell silent, he said in a thunderous voice: 'Do you confess?'

I tried to stand up, but the guards knocked me down on my knees. Kneeling, I cried:

'Honourable judge, there must be some mistake, why I do not even know a Chu Cheng.'

The judge frowned and ordered the scribe to refresh my memory and read Chu Cheng's accusation. And so I learned that a certain Chu Cheng had turned to the court with the humble plea that the villainy of the administrator of the district, named Wang, who had sullied his good name, be punished. Chu Cheng had been a subordinate of the afore-said Wang, and at his command he had implicated himself in the trafficking of antiques. But then when the inspectors came into the district, Wang blamed everything on Chu, who was not even fully aware of what had been going on. In disgrace Chu was instantly removed. He was so tormented by his humiliation and by the loss of his good reputation, that he died of grief. Afterwards, he accused administrator Wang of depriving him of his good reputation, and with that, being responsible for his untimely death.

While the scribe monotonously read the accusation and the judge fastened his threatening stare on me, I realized that it was indeed a mistake. Why, I was never the administrator of this district, but held a position in the province. And so when I was again called on to express myself with regards to the accusation, I tried to convince the judge that there were after all a great many Wangs. I had never held the post of administrator of the district, and I was truly not acquainted with any Chu Cheng. But you know how it is in officialdom. The judge ordered me to be taken to prison until the whole case was made clear. And when it came to light that it was indeed a matter of a different Wang, who is not to die until tomorrow, exactly a quarter of a year after my death, two full months went by. Then I was freed and I came back here. Except that I found myself in the devilish situation that I have already described to you.'

Yeh listened with great interest to Wang's narration and exacted further and further details from him of the underworld court proceedings. They examined the case from all angles, the night slipped past and beyond the windows, day began to dawn. Wang arose to go and thanked his friend for his help in his distress. Then he added just in passing:

'Perhaps it will interest you that that Wang is Wang Lüe, the administrator of this very district where you are carrying on an inspection.'

Wang finished speaking and vanished in the same way as he had appeared. Yeh Nin-fei dozed off for a while. When he awoke, servants brought him the news that the district administrator Wang had died suddenly during the night. Yeh asked that he be submitted all the old documents, and after careful study he confirmed that a certain Chu Cheng had indeed worked in the district office for many years before, and he had been deprived of his rank for fraudulent dealings with antiques. Chu had died shortly afterwards of grief and disgrace.

Toward evening Yeh Nin-fei set off to the monastery at the city walls and there he burned sacrificial paper money for his friend Wang.

When Yeh finished his inspection in the Hua-si district, he returned again to his own office. On the way, however, he stopped at the birth-place of his friend and bowed at his grave. In the evening Wang again came to visit him and thanked him for his help. They talked amicably for a long time, and as they were parting, Wang revealed to him that the other Wang had already been sentenced by the underworld judge. As his punishment, in his next life he was to be reborn in the image of a pig.

The Head
of an Ancient
Hero

Amiran, son of the hunter Sulkamakh and of the forest goddess Dali, enjoyed roaming through his native land accompanied by his two brothers Badr and Usip battling against demons, tyrants and villains, for they hated all evil. All three were excellent men and the people loved them for themselves as well as for their bravery. There was always a place for them at the tables of ordinary people. There were no towns in the land and the three heroes stayed away from castles, not wishing to seek hospitality amongst their foes. Very often they were in places where there was no shelter to be had, and this meant that Amiran and his brothers spent the night under the open sky, sheltered against foul weather by nothing more than their felt cloaks.

Once it happened that they were travelling over a deserted plain when evening caught up with them. A strange shaped rock stood on the horizon. A storm was brewing and there was no sign of the light of a human dwelling. Then Amiran said:

'Brothers, let us go to that cliff which we see. It is quite possible that we will find an overhanging rock where we can shelter through the coming night.'

As he said, so they did. When they drew near the cliff heavy rain began to fall and it was impossible to think of spending the night on the open plain. They could see two caves in the cliff, spacious enough to accommodate three riders and their horses. And they rode towards it, and led their horses into one of the caves and built a fire on its floor. They dried their cloaks by the fire and prepared their meal. Then they spread out their cloaks, and without considering that they should take turns standing guard, they slept the sleep of the just.

Then, on the following day, when they were preparing to

set off on their travels again, Amiran, son of Dali, said:

'Look, brothers, that was not a cliff where we spent the night, but the skull of a warrior with a helmet. The cave where the three of us slept with our horses was one of the empty eye sockets in that skull.'

And Amiran's brothers Badr and Usip looked up, and they said:

'You are not mistaken, brother Amiran.'

And they decided to ride around the entire cliff, which was the head of an ancient hero, to marvel at its enormity.

After they had done so, Amiran said again:

'This is certainly one of the people who lived long before us. I would very much like to talk to him, to learn about his brave deeds and about what misfortune overtook him that he now stands buried to his head in the earth.'

'Perhaps you might succeed if you prayed to the all-powerful God,' suggested Badr and Usip.

And Amiran looked to the heavens and recited this prayer:

'All-powerful God, who decides over life and death, bring this man before us back to life.'

But before he could finish his prayer, Badr interrupted him with these words:

'Let only his head come to life.'

Amiran was surprised, but he added 'Amen'.

All of a sudden the colossal bones were covered with flesh, under the helmet grew thick curls, and there, where the empty sockets had been, appeared closed eyes with long lashes under ominous brows.

And all three brothers, wondrous at this miracle which they had called forth, turned their horses and rode some distance away. Then they turned their faces again towards the giant who was looking now to one side, now to the other, swivelling his huge glittering eyes.

Then he opened his enormous mouth under its black mustachios, his white teeth flashed, and he asked:

'Who has brought me back to life?'

'Almighty God brought you back to life at our request,' Amiran answered him.

'Who are you?' the giant asked again.

'We are humans,' said Amiran.

'If you are humans, where are you that I cannot see you?'

'Here we are,' called out Amiran, 'directly in front of you.'

The giant looked in the direction of the voice, but it was apparent that strain his eyes as he might, he did not see anyone.

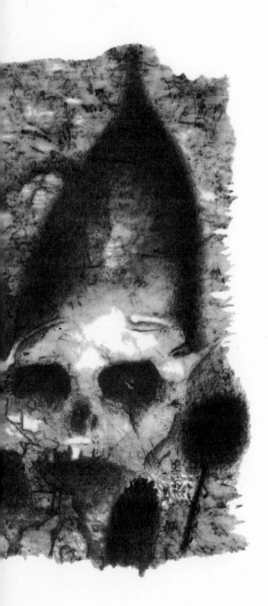

Then all three brothers spurred their horses, making them rear up, and shouting and waving their hats in the air, they rode toward the head.

'Oh, there you are, you little specks, who are crawling in front of my nose like flies on a table. You must have to be very careful indeed that other humans do not squash you underfoot, when you travel along the roads,' said the giant.

'We are no smaller than other humans, no one can squash us underfoot,' said Amiran.

'Do you mean to say, little speck, that all humans today look like you?' the giant said in astonishment.

'Only very few attain our stature and our strength,' replied Amiran.

'Poor little things,' said the giant, 'no doubt that is because you do not eat properly. What do you eat, by the way?'

'We eat what we hunt and what we cultivate in our fields,' said Amiran.

'You probably have bad fields,' said the giant, 'and the largest animals in your forests are probably ants and tiny insects that live in flowers. Do you know what, little speck? Let me taste something of your food, so that I can see whether it gives you much nourishment.'

Amiran reached into his satchel, to give the giant some bread and cheese, but Badr stopped him.

'Give him a rock,' he whispered to him.

And Amiran picked a big boulder up from the ground and thrust it between the lips of the giant.

The giant crunched the stone with his strong teeth, and it shattered into a pile of gravel.

'You feed yourselves with a poor diet indeed,' said the giant. 'No wonder that you are so tiny as a result. Why, we used to eat simple pancakes and cheese and drank it down with wine. That is why we were big and strong. If we had eaten what you eat, we would hardly have achieved all that we achieved.'

'And what did you achieve?' asked Amiran.

'We fought against demons, tyrants and villains, for we hated evil very much,' replied the giant.

'We too fight,' said Amiran.

'How can you fight?' asked the giant in amazement, 'why a hundred of the strongest among you could barely lift the smallest of weapons. Perhaps you little ones can bite and scratch, but what can you achieve with that? Give me your hand, little crumb, so I can see whether you have at least a little strength in your arms.'

Amiran stepped forward to give him his hand. But Badr whispered:

'Hand him the strong branch of a tree.'

Amiran picked up a mighty oak branch and placed it between the giant's lips. The giant barely touched it with his tongue and the branch shattered into splinters.

'Poor little things,' declared the giant, 'it is as I thought, that with such a diet you could not be worth much. Why in our day there were people who could bend horseshoes with their bare hands, and it was child's play for them to set an overturned wagon right with their shoulders.'

Amiran, son of Dali, and his brothers Badr and Usip only opened their mouths in wonder and were silent.

Then the giant declared:

'Arrange it so I am dead again. I do not want to look at this world, full of puny little wretches. Perhaps one day you will learn to cultivate your fields properly, then you will eat more substantially and grow stronger. Then later, after a hundred generations, someone will come again and bring me back to life and joyfully I shall arise and return to my work. But now I would rather be a skeleton with empty sockets instead of eyes.'

When he heard this, Amiran prayed again to the all-powerful God:

'Almighty God, who decides over life and death, make this giant what he was before you brought him back to life at our request.'

Badr and Usip added:

'Amen!'

And the brothers descended and left him as a rock to his dreams of long ago.

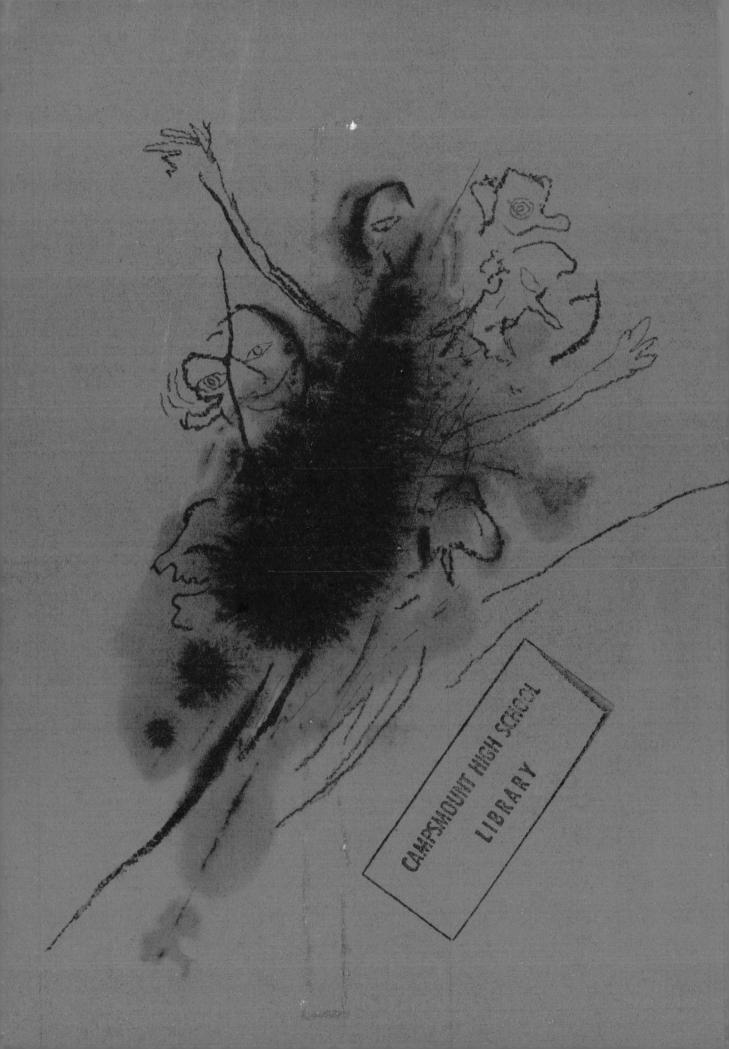